SCIENCE

AND

HUMAN LIFE

SCIENCE

AND

HUMAN LIFE

by
J. A. V. BUTLER

BASIC BOOKS, INC.
Publishers, New York

$$\frac{B}{B}$$

First Printing, 1957

Second Printing, 1958

Published in the United States of America

by Basic. Books, Inc., by arrangement with

PERGAMON PRESS

Library of Congress Catalog Card Number: 57-9748

TO LOIS

PREFACE

AT THE present time, when so many ancient barriers imposed by geography have been annihilated by the progress of communications, and huge populations in many parts of the world are absorbing, or attempting to absorb and to use for their own purposes, the substance of western science, technology, and politics, and as a result are awakening to a new feeling of their destiny, and an urge to play an important part on the world stage, we are clearly on the brink of great adjustments and changes, of which no one can predict the outcome.

It is a time when many contradictory views of human nature are being put forward and acted upon; an epoch which has been marked by the most fiendish cruelty, practised for political purposes on a scale probably unequalled in any previous age; and at the same time an epoch when quite sincere and to some extent successful efforts to solve difficult problems by reason and with justice have been made. It is then not inappropriate to ask the old questions—*What are we?*, *What is the basis of human life?*—and to try to discover what science, which has revealed so much of the constitution of the universe, can contribute to the answer.

It is, as we shall see, too much to claim that science can provide definite answers, but it is certain that in the last few decades much new information has been obtained which has enlarged our knowledge both of life in general and human life in particular. The scientific findings have not been well assimilated, and in fact the current views of what science has discovered are often far too superficial and glib not to be misleading. This book is a personal attempt to put recent discoveries into some perspective and to discuss their human implications.

The new knowledge is derived from many specialized branches of science, and although there are many who have an expert knowledge of one or two of them, no one can have more than a superficial knowledge of the whole. The author is well aware of the dangers of venturing outside his own speciality, and that he may be told that like the cobbler he should stick to his last. However, if it is conceded that a wide view is desirable, it is not easy to see who should undertake it. Perhaps the only real qualification is interest; and the author can only claim that, if he has spent a good many years in studying some corners of science, he has always maintained a curiosity, and perhaps too great an interest, in other aspects of human knowledge.

I need only add that this interpretation of current trends in science has grown as it proceeded, and has taken directions and led me to conclusions I certainly did not foresee when it started.

Finally, I should like to express my thanks to Dr P. Rosbaud, not only for detailed comments, which helped to bring the manuscript into its final state, but also for more general help. I also thank Mr E. J. Buckley and Mr H. C. Warner of the Pergamon Press for their unfailing helpfulness.

J. A. V. B.

LONDON, 27 *July* 1956

Contents

SCIENCE AND THE INDIVIDUAL

Chapter One

SCIENCE AND THE IDEA
OF HUMAN NATURE

The character of all our human institutions depends both
on what man *is* and in equal and greater measure upon
what we humans *think* man is.
C. T. KEYSER, *Mathematical Philosophy:*
a Study of Fate and Freedom

THE OBJECT of this book is to discuss what has been learnt from
science about the basic problems of life and mind, and to trace the
impact of science on the idea of human nature and to see where it
seems to be leading. I want to ask if we have obtained, or can
expect to obtain, from scientific study, a complete and reliable
knowledge of the nature of man.

Before the scientific era human beings thought of themselves as
the dominant figures in a universe in which all other forms of life
appeared to have been made solely for their use and enjoyment.
Science first displaced the earth from its central position in the
universe; later it did much to displace man from his unique
position among living things. He became merely a member of the
animal kingdom—perhaps the most distinguished one, but only
the winner of the battle of the survival of the fittest, a contest in
which the winning cards were dealt by chance.

This was the picture of man which nineteenth-century science
arrived at; the twentieth century has gone much further in undermining human dignity. The progress of chemistry has revealed
human beings as chemical mechanisms, which operate to a considerable extent under the influence of their endocrine glands.
The progress of brain physiology has seemed to show them to be
automata—their brains being perhaps capable of a greater variety
of tricks than the present-day electronic calculating machines, but
certainly operating much more slowly. Then Freud and his

followers did much to destroy the idea of man as a rational creature; he was exhibited as an irrational and impulsive creature, and it appeared that nearly all his impulses were controlled by sex.

In all these ways science in the twentieth century has undermined the basic concept of human nature on which western ideas of justice, the rights of man, and even ordinary human relations were based.

Now, on the whole, the scientific discoveries have to be accepted. They may be modified in detail, and they will undoubtedly be extended, but there is no doubt that as facts they have come to stay. The question I wish to discuss is whether the conclusions which are drawn from them are justified.

The question is not an academic one. It is practical and necessary because, in the last resort, our attitude to all human questions depends on our idea of human nature.

If, for example, we think that human beings are just chemical mechanisms—robots which work out automatic responses to the signals they receive, through their eyes and ears, in their calculating-machine brains—we will, in the long run, take a different view about what is permissible with human beings than if we accept the view, which is implicit in most religions, that there is something in man over and above the mechanical and the material.

We will also behave differently if we picture ourselves as the *Homo sapiens* of the nineteenth century—that is, as individuals with reasoning ability and a sense of responsibility—than if we think of ourselves as a kind of super-monkey, animals with a veneer of intellect, which are subject to irrational and uncontrollable urges.

It is necessary to make some sort of judgement of these different theories, because they lead to different kinds of human society and to different sets of values. Indeed everyone has to accept one view or another of human nature. Even if we do not think about it, our general outlook will be moulded around the prevailing idea of it. Certainly, at the present time, when two kinds of political system, based on quite different views of human nature, are competing for world supremacy, we can hardly avoid the issue.

Scientific discoveries have greatly affected human ways of living and the background of human experience. All sorts of attitudes towards this new knowledge exist, from fear and contempt to an almost idolatrous respect. Some people regard science as a destructive agency, which is bound to destroy civilization, because it has let loose forces too powerful to be controlled. Others see no limit to its ability to solve the problems of human life. They think that scientific knowledge is capable of solving all human problems.

It is true that in recent years our knowledge of biology has been very greatly increased, and that the gap between the living and the nonliving is not nearly as wide as it once seemed to be. In fact, we find an almost unbroken sequence from the nonliving to the living, and it is hard to say where life begins. The description of living things as chemical systems is much more complete than it used to be, although no one would claim it is anything like perfect. This has given strong support to the materialistic view of life, and no doubt most biochemists and physiologists would say that they see living things as complex mechanisms. They do not completely understand these mechanisms, it is true—but, nevertheless, they expect to find nothing in them which cannot be explained in terms of the ordinary behaviour of chemical substances.

At the same time there has been something of a revulsion among physicists and mathematicians from the rigid materialism of the late nineteenth century. The atoms of matter are no longer thought of as hard, impenetrable bodies. Matter itself has been resolved into something that can only be described in very abstract symbols, which are themselves creations of pure thought. Hence the idea, advocated by Jeans and Eddington, that the underlying substratum of the universe is something not entirely different in nature from thought.

There is thus an extraordinary divergence of outlook even among scientists. It is rather curious that the biologists should be more mechanically minded than the physicists, but this probably arises from the more elementary state of biological knowledge. Biology is still at a stage where simple mechanical explanations are adequate, although of course there is much that is not well understood.

Scientific studies of human society have also made much progress, although they began much later than the study of the physical world (they are, in fact, barely a hundred years old): and although human society in its variety and complication presents an entirely different kind of problem, so that such studies lack the certainty which is found in other branches of science, they have had a considerable impact on our ideas of human nature and an appreciable influence on current politics and morals.

The main effect of studies of the numerous uncivilized communities in many parts of the world, which exist or have existed, until quite recently, has been to throw doubt on the necessity of our own standards and customs. If the Polynesians could live what appears to be a perfectly good life with a totally different set of sexual and social taboos, what is the necessity behind ours? Judgements of human institutions therefore appeared to be purely relative—and variable. It was impossible to say that one way of life was better than another—it was merely a question of use and habit, of how you were brought up.

So in the later part of this book I shall come to discuss the wider issues of human life. Are we to suppose that we now have a fairly complete and adequate scientific picture of life in general and man in particular, which can be used as a guide in the problems of human living? Even if we accept, as we obviously must, that science has greatly increased our knowledge of the human organism and also of human communities, we have to ask how far this knowledge is useful in the wider questions which confront human society. Can human life be based on scientifically ascertained knowledge? Can it be claimed that by scientific study of the conditions of human life we could arrive at solutions of all human problems, or shall we find that it is still necessary to have beliefs which go beyond what can be scientifically proved?

I must begin by explaining what the essence of the scientific method is and how it has been able to change the human outlook so radically.

Chapter Two

SCIENCE AND THE INANIMATE WORLD

Science aims at constructing a world which shall be
symbolic of the world of commonplace experience.
A. S. EDDINGTON, *The Nature of the Physical World*

Why think? Why not try the experiment.
JOHN HUNTER to EDWARD JENNER

THE SECRET of science, which began in the fourteenth century as
a new way of looking at things, was to isolate very simple phenomena, like the motion of a ball thrown in the air, and then to find
simple models which would reproduce their main features. The
facts were not new for the most part. What was new was the
approach—what Professor Butterfield calls a new 'thinking-cap'
applied to old knowledge.

The first success of this method came in a region which might
have been expected to be one of the last to be successfully explored
—the study of the motions of the planets. The reason for this
success was that the laws of motion are exhibited here in their
very simplest forms, uncomplicated by the many extraneous factors
like friction and air resistance, which affect the motion of objects
on earth, and which made it difficult to discover the simple laws
of motion from observations on falling bodies and on projectiles.

The successful discovery of the laws of planetary motion was primarily due to the fact that a set of abstract patterns was available
which were suitable for the description of planetary motions. The
Greek geometers had discovered the basic geometrical forms like
straight lines, circles, ellipses, and so forth and had worked out
many of their properties. The Arab mathematicians had provided
in algebra a method which made detailed calculations possible.
It was then possible to see in the motions of the planets, with not
too great an effort of the imagination, the circles and ellipses of the

B

mathematicians. It was the conjunction of the exact study of planetary motions with the existence of patterns which were capable of accommodating them which established the method of science and in the end made the inanimate universe understandable.

Before this, the motions of the sun and the planets had been supposed to be governed by a complicated machinery of heavenly spheres, which moved according to the Ptolomaic system in a subtle ethereal fluid without friction, in very complex cycles and epicycles. This was the orthodox belief of the mediaeval Church. It was sometimes thought that these machines were operated by celestial intelligences, but Jean Buredon had pointed out in the middle of the fourteenth century that it was quite unnecessary to imagine such intelligences, for the whole machine, once started, would run by itself.

Then Copernicus in 1543 showed that a much simpler interpretation could be given to the planetary movements, if it were supposed that the earth and the planets were moving independently round the sun in more or less circular orbits. The Church did not at first object but regarded it as a harmless mathematical device for making calculations. Indeed, Copernicus did not claim that his system was true in a physical sense, but merely that it was a mathematically simpler representation of the observations. As one writer has said, 'It took fifty years to see that Copernicus was bound to lead to Voltaire.'*

Copernicus's theory led to the improved observations of Tycho Brahe, which were studied by the mathematician, Kepler, who deduced from them the correct mathematical forms. He found that the orbits of the planets could be described more accurately as ellipses than as circles round the sun, and that a planet moved more quickly the nearer it was to the sun. He believed in the harmony of numbers and looked for and found a simple relation between the distances of the planets from the sun and their periods of revolution. Then Galileo, who was the first practical physicist, made himself a telescope and discovered a miniature version of the solar system in Jupiter and its moons. This was enough to convince him of the correctness of the

---

* P. G. Frank. *Modern Science and its philosophy* (Oxford University Press).

Copernican theory and, jumping into theology, he attempted to prove that the Copernican system was not inconsistent with Scripture. But this was too much for the Church, which had now become aware of the danger to the orthodox Ptolemaic view, and Galileo was forced to recant, although there is some doubt whether he really abandoned his theory.

Notwithstanding Kepler's discovery of relations between the rates of revolution of the planets and their distances from the sun, a convincing explanation of their motion was still unknown. Why did they move at these rates? Why did bodies fall to the earth at a certain speed? These questions were unanswered until Newton, one of the most profound thinkers of all time, succeeded by linking the true laws of motion which had been adumbrated by Galileo with the facts of terrestrial and planetary motions. These laws invoked a very abstract idea, which can only with difficulty be realized by experiment—that of a body moving without any frictional resistance. Such a body continues to move at a uniform speed without the application of any force, but when a force is applied it produces a change of velocity.

Newton showed that with these laws of motion, together with the law of gravitation (attraction between bodies at a distance), it was possible to account equally well for movements of falling bodies on the earth and for the motions of the planets. The same forces as those which cause the fall of the apple in the orchard also moved the planets, and the law governing both motions was a universal one.

Science thus found its *open sesame* in doing to the external world of nature what, in a cruder way, we all do to our raw sensations,* namely to find the abstract patterns to which observed phenomena can be fitted. The chief difference between ordinary interpretations of experience and the scientific ones is that the scientific patterns are not always easy to find; so it is not surprising that they were first found, where they appear in their greatest simplicity, in the slow and apparently intricate movements of the planets.

The appropriate pattern or model for a natural happening is

---

* See Chapter Seven for an explanation of this.

often not at all obvious to common sense; but when it has been found and when it has been demonstrated that it really fits the phenomenon, we feel that we understand what is happening and why. The model is often directly useful in that it leads to successful predictions of the unknown.

In this method of investigation, Galileo and Newton clearly laid down the method which physical science was to follow for the next 250 years. The ability to see natural phenomena from this new point of view, to perform experiments in which the phenomena were exhibited in as simple a form as possible, and then to make a mental model which could be handled mathematically—this was the new approach which in time made many of the workings of the physical world understandable.

Later on electric and magnetic forces were added to the gravitational force, and by the end of the nineteenth century it appeared that a complete explanation of the physical universe might be obtained in terms of these forces acting between the ultimate atoms of matter. All that seemed to be left to do was to make more accurate calculations and to deal with greater and greater assemblies of atoms. Lord Kelvin put the nineteenth-century point of view very clearly when he said, 'It seems to me that the test of "Do we understand a particular point in physics?" is "Can we make a mechanical model of it?" '

The effect of this new approach to nature on the western world has been very great. It had, of course, great practical consequences. It provided that understanding of motion and power, which was necessary for the management of concentrated sources of power. Without Newton's laws of motion, the tremendous development of machines and engines, which was responsible for the industrial revolution, could hardly have taken place.

But it also gave rise to a revolution in human thought. The success of Newton's laws of motion was a convincing demonstration of the rationality of the universe, which no longer appeared to be capricious and arbitrary, but the scene of understandable laws and a region in which accurate predictions could be made. It was true that many phenomena, like winds and storms, were still far too complex to be susceptible to simple calculations like those applicable to the motions of the planets. Nevertheless

Newton's laws were generalized by Lagrange and Laplace to cover systems of many bodies. The difficulty here was not one of principle, but merely of handling many factors at once in the calculations.

As a result of this development all natural phenomena were seen to be the result of the interactions of swarms of particles acting on each other with definite forces, obeying known laws. The universe was thought of as having developed from an original swarm of particles which, under the influence of their own forces, had given rise to suns, planets, and satellites. It appeared to be completely mechanical. Every event was predetermined; that is, was the necessary result of the forces acting and there was no place in it for free will or volition.

The material universe was in this way brought within the scope of human understanding. To Jean Fernel, writing in 1548, nature was an expression of the will and order of God. 'Nature,' he says, 'embracing all things and entering into each, governs the courses and the revolutions of the sun and moon and of the other stars, and the succession of times, the change of the season, and ebb and flow of the ocean. Nature rules this immensity of things with an order assured and unvarying. How were it possible for nature so to conduct and direct all this thus well, but for the interposition of a divine Intelligence, which having produced the world, preserves it?' In short, nature is under God's direction.*

Two hundred years later, as a result of the scientific revolution, natural happenings were thought of as being brought about by the action of natural laws without outside interference. Nature was regarded as a closed system containing the causes of events within itself. Once started, the whole thing would go on by itself indefinitely. This greatly reduced the region in which the Deity could be supposed to act, and was a very powerful factor in undermining religious belief. But the great thinkers were under no doubt about the existence of powers which they did not understand and which did not come within the scheme. It was still necessary to invoke a 'prime mover' to get the whole system started. There were also living things which were obstinately different and

---

* Quoted in Sherrington, *Man on his Nature.*

apparently capable of influencing events in the inanimate world.

The Newtonian scheme seemed to be adequate at least to explain the working of the inanimate world, as it exists and it was only at the end of the nineteenth century that phenomena were met with which could not be fitted into it. The discovery of radioactivity by Becquerel and the Curies revealed something which was quite beyond the scope of nineteenth-century models, and which could only be explained if the atoms of matter were themselves disintegrating with an evolution of energy of magnitudes hitherto unsuspected. The first subatomic particle, the electron, was discovered by Sir J. J. Thomson. Later other particles were discovered and it became clear that the behaviour of such elementary particles and also single atoms was very different to that of the massive bodies previously studied. The emission and absorption of light gave rise to similar difficulties. Light, so long regarded as a wave motion, was found to be emitted and absorbed in quanta— little packets of energy obeying strange laws. The new world of atomic physics could not be assimilated by the engineers' models of the nineteenth century, or indeed by any models which could be visualized.

Physicists have met this situation by abandoning the use of concrete models; they are content to express the results in mathematical, equations to which no easily 'visualized' meaning can be given. Moreover these equations express only statistical averages or probabilities. We cannot say when any one radioactive atom will explode: all we know is that in any time interval a certain number of the atoms will explode. We have no means of distinguishing those atoms which will explode in the next minute from those which will explode in a year or a hundred years. Thus on an atomic scale our ordinary ideas of cause and effect have no meaning.

It may be, as Einstein thought, that this is merely due to our ignorance of the nature of the subatomic world and the time may come when we have explanations for these events, similar to the explanations which Newton's laws of motion provided for the movements of massive bodies. But at present this has not been achieved, and in the opinion of many mathematical physicists it is impossible, in the nature of things, to have such laws. We have empirical and useful laws which express behaviour, and on a large scale behaviour is predictable; but in the world of atoms and radiation the old rigid determinism has gone. All we find is a flux of matter and energy which is amenable to calculation to some extent and is expressible by numbers. In fact, we have a return to the Pythagorian view that the universe at the bottom displays the combinations of pure numbers.

It is obvious then that the physicists' view of the universe in the twentieth century is very different to that taken at the end of the nineteenth century. The universe cannot be regarded as in principle completely known; indeed what we see and know appears to arise from happenings in an underlying region of which the laws are still unknown, and may perhaps be unknowable because of the crudity of our instruments and the fact, as Heisenberg pointed out, that there are some things we cannot know because at the atomic level the fact of observation disturbs the things which are to be observed.

Before we turn to the world of life there are some other features of the scientific movement which will repay attention. The scientific approach is natural and congenial to the human mind, because it uses those faculties which human beings necessarily use in the ordinary business of living—viz. accurate observation, comparison, and an effort to distinguish the important from the unimportant. The scientist no doubt uses these abilities in a more intense and purposeful manner than most people for he is a person with a passion for making distinctions and a strong desire to co-ordinate his experience into a generalized picture or model.

However, science is not *essentially* an 'intellectual' occupation— it is humble and plodding in its approach. Its chief characteristic is an interest in diverse phenomena, and no phenomenon is so trivial as to be beneath its notice. Simple experiments with amber and pith balls led to the discovery of static electricity; and in more recent times the observation of Becquerel, that some substances like uranium could affect a photographic plate through paper, led to the discovery of radioactivity.

Science began as a protest against the endless and often pointless disputations of scholars. As Whitehead has pointed out, scientific theory is not essentially a *rational* construction, i.e. it is not an abstract system of relationships which are put together by taking thought. The mediaeval schoolmen could and did debate about many things, such as what happened when an irresistible force met an immovable object, or the incompatible qualities of fire and water, or the opposing principles of weight and levity, or the number of angels who could sit on the point of a needle. Scientific progress began to be made in fact when it was thought worth while to study apparently trivial phenomena, without relating them to the whole background of knowledge. The scientists took an interest in the curious happenings of the everyday world—often those which had a practical application. If you turn over the pages of the early volumes of the *Transactions of the Royal Society* you will find many papers which exhibit this simple curiosity about phenomena, and interest in new devices, as is shown by the following titles taken almost at random:

An account of the improvement of Optic Glasses in Rome; Of a peculiar Lead Ore in Germany; New Observations and experiments in order to compile an Experimental History of cold; Of a way of killing Rattlesnakes; New Pneumatical Experiments about Respiration, made and communicated by the Honourable Robert Boyle; Observations upon the Barometer, or Ballance of the Air; New Experiments concerning the relation between Light and Air (in Shining Wood and Fish) made by the Honourable Robert Boyle.

Science began to be successful when the models available were sufficiently abstract to accommodate experience. The great difficulty in science has always been to find sufficiently abstract models, and the great scientific discoverers have been those rare individuals who can see the essential simplicity in a welter of separate happenings and devise an abstract framework which will accommodate not only the known facts, but will be an inspiration for the discovery of new ones. A real scientific discovery does far more than explain the phenomena which its inventor knew about; it is found to be the model of many new phenomena; examples of it are found everywhere in nature.

John Dalton went about poking into marshes and collecting the gases which came bubbling up from decaying vegetable matter. From his analysis of these gases he evolved his *atomic* theory, which has guided the work of chemists ever since because all the compounds which have since been made have been found to fit simply into this theory. It was a plan or model of the construction of chemical compounds which has been found to be capable of the greatest extension.

Again, when Sir Alexander Fleming discovered in penicillin the first antibiotic (a chemical substance produced by a fungus to kill parasitic bacteria), it was then found that the natural world contained numerous substances of the same kind; they had only to be looked for.

An important element in science has always been the combination of observation and experiment. Science really began when philosophers tried to do experiments which would tell them what happens when the circumstances are arranged as far as possible to isolate one factor, as when Galileo dropped balls of different weights from a high tower and Newton experimented with the effects of glass prisms on beams of light. But experiments by themselves are not enough; the experiment is always suggested by a theory and may be designed to prove or disprove it. The willingness to submit theories to experiment has been a necessary part of the scientific outlook.

The third point about science is that it is a co-operative effort and necessarily depends on communication of the results. It has always depended on methods being available for the dissemination of scientific results, either through societies in which members meet for free discussion, or journals in which the results of scientific work are published. It is essential for the progress of science that all observations should be offered for critical study and all theories for criticism. It is only after confirmation by others that scientific results are accepted as facts, and it is only when scientific theories are admitted to be a reasonable interpretation of the facts that they are regarded as acceptable, and even then it is open to anyone to propose a new theory which fits the facts better or to bring forward new observations which may or may not fit in.

Science has progressed and has led to a vast extension of know-

ledge precisely because it submits all its observations to the judgement of the general body of scientists. It is like the co-operative
painting of an enormous picture by a large number of people.
Some are concerned with filling in details here and there. Others
are mapping out possible designs on the blank canvas. When they
have made a tentative sketch they stand back and let others look
at their work. They ask, is this inevitable and right? Does it fit
in with the plans which others are making on other parts of the
canvas? If it seems good and necessary it is adopted as the basis
of further explorations.

Science has been successful just because it established a means
of combining the efforts of many individuals in the study of
natural phenomena, a project which has always been too vast an
undertaking for any one person to study with any hope of success.
The intellectual efforts of the Greeks were clearly equal to those
of any other age and the reason that they did not progress farther
in science, after making all the necessary and basic mathematical
abstractions, is probably the lack of this basic machinery of co-
operation. Possibly, also, they did not have the patience and
interest to study apparently trivial effects and curious phenomena.

The effect of science in the world has been much greater than
the knowledge gained. It released the human mind from the world
of hobgoblins and nameless fears it often lived in, and made it
conscious of its own ability. It upset the whole mediaeval system
of theology. When it was no longer necessary to believe that
God directed natural happenings, it was not a big step to the
idea that he did not control and was disinterested in human
beings as well. If this were so, many of the sanctions on which
social and political life was based disappeared.

It also set up a new standard of judgement which has permeated
much of civilized life. A statement is not accepted merely because
it is made on authority. An attempt is first made to establish what
the facts are and secondly what conclusions can be drawn from
them. There have always been great regions of experience in
which the facts are inadequately known and so no conclusions can
be drawn. This has led naturally to an agnostic frame of mind;
confronted with something outside his experience the scientist
just says that this problem has not been studied and therefore he

can give no opinion. We shall come later to consider the limitations which such an attitude must have in the practical problems of human life.

So from this very brief review of how science has dealt with the inanimate world, we turn to the world of life and see how it has attempted to explain what it found there.

Chapter Three

SCIENTIFIC VIEWS OF LIFE

THE METHOD of science, as we have seen, was to make simplified models of natural phenomena, which could be manipulated mentally and so understood. The objects most like these scientific models were machines, such as clocks, water wheels and windmills, so that it was natural for men of science to compare nature with machinery and (since machines can do some of the things which living organisms can do) to look for examples of mechanism in life. They found them in plenty. The limbs and muscles of animals were thought of as examples of levers and pulleys, as illustrated in the drawings of Leonardo da Vinci. Harvey discovered the function of the heart as a pump forcing the blood through the blood vessels. The lungs were bellows for drawing in fresh air, and so on.

All this made a tremendous impression on the thinkers of the time. If inanimate nature was the realm of natural law, why not living things too, and why should man be exempt? Even before Newton, Descartes (1596-1650) had tried to bring all phenomena into a coherent mechanical philosophy. 'The body of a man', he said, 'is nothing but a statue or machine made of earth.' Leibnitz (1646-1716), a contemporary of Newton, went further with the words, 'The body of a man is as mechanical as that which takes place in a watch.'

Nevertheless, Descartes was willing to concede the existence of a soul, a 'ghost within the machine', which received the perceptions from the senses and acted as the organ of the will. He thought that the liaison between the soul and the body was effected in the pineal gland, presumably chosen because of its central position in the brain. Others thought the soul was unnecessary—the brain received the sense impressions and worked out the proper responses. This was the beginning of the conflict between 'mechanical' and 'vitalist' views of life, which went on for many years.

Before coming to that, I shall outline the scientific picture of life and living things, which was arrived at as the result of the efforts of students of natural history of the eighteenth and nineteenth centuries. But first of all we might note that, when originally stated, the mechanical view of a living organism was little more than an expression of belief in the uniformity of nature, that living bodies were not outside the realm of natural laws. What was actually known about living things was ludicrously inadequate to support *any* view as to their real nature. There were, it is true, some resemblances between some of the contrivances of living things and machines, but to push this analogy to the point of declaring that the body of a man was a machine was, at the time, a declaration of faith that the method which had successfully dealt with the laws of motion and gravity (and not much else) would one day be able to interpret living tissue.

At this time there was no scientific knowledge of the nature of living bodies. Chemistry was embryonic. So far from knowing what the body of a man was made of, science could give no coherent account of simple substances like salt and water, of burning, of the nature of air, or of many other everyday phenomena.

Although the exploration of living things as molecular systems made such slow progress, great efforts were made to discover *laws* of animate nature similar to those of the inanimate. It was obvious to students of natural history that living nature was not planless, although the lines of the plan were obscure. Extensive studies of the structure of living things led to the main lines of classification being drawn up, especially by Linnaeus (1707-1778), who made a classification of all living forms in his *System of Nature*. This caused him to overemphasize the distinctions and barriers between species, which he thought of as immutable. 'There are just so many species as there were forms created in the beginning,' he said; but later in his life he was willing to admit a certain amount of overlapping.

The likenesses between similar species were too great, however, to be overlooked, and the idea of a common origin of diverse living forms suggested itself to a number of thinkers. Immanuel Kant (1729-1804) thought that the fact that so many animals are built on a similar plan 'strengthens the supposition that they have an actual blood relationship due to derivation from a common parent, a supposition which is arrived at by observations . . . extending from man down to the polyps and from these even down to mosses and lichens and arriving finally at raw matter, the lowest stage of nature observable by us. From this raw matter and its forces the whole apparatus of nature seems to have been derived according to mechanical laws (such as those which resulted in the production of crystals); yet this apparatus as seen is so incomprehensible to us that we feel ourselves compelled to conceive for it a different principle.'

Note the urge to bring organized beings into the realm of inanimate laws. The basic knowledge required for its realization was still lacking and remained so for many years. Nevertheless there is a clear recognition here of organized creatures and even man being part of nature and not distinct from it and superimposed on it. Numerous attempts were made to suggest how the multiplicity of species came into existence and to find a natural origin for them. Kant's contemporary, George Louis le Clerc Buffon (1707-1788), (the 'celebrated Buffoon' of *Back to Methuselah*) also tried to bring all living things into a system and did not shrink from ascribing a natural origin to life—a spontaneous generation in the Polar ocean ages ago. He speaks of species 'being perfected or degenerated, by the great changes in land and sea, by the favours or disfavours of nature, by food, by the prolonged influence of climate, contrary or favourable.'

Erasmus Darwin (1731-1802), a doctor of Derby, was a follower of Buffon, and like his predecessors criticized the idea of a special creation for every form of life and was impressed by the many similarities of living things and their exact adaptation to the environment. 'When we revolve the metamorphoses of animals' he said, 'as from the tadpole to the frog; secondly the changes produced by artificial cultivation, as in the breeds of horses, dogs and sheep; thirdly, the changes produced by the conditions of climate and of season, as in the sheep of warm climates being covered with hair instead of wool, and the hares and partridges of northern climates becoming white in winter; when farther we observe the changes of structure produced by habit as seen especially in men of different occupations, or the changes produced by artificial mutilation, and prenatal influences, as in the crossing of species and production of monsters; fourthly, when we observe the essential unity of plan of all warm-blooded animals, we are led to conclude that they have been alike produced from a similar living filament.' He summed up his belief in the following words: 'The world has been evolved, not created; it has arisen little by little from a small beginning and has increased through the activity of the elemental forces within itself, and so has rather grown than come into being at an almighty word. What a sublime sign of the infinite might of the great Architect, the Cause of all causes, the Father of all fathers, the *Ens Entium*.'

This was a remarkably clear statement of the occurrence of evolution, but it did not explain how such changes took place. Enquiring minds asked what were the 'elemental forces' which produced such an extraordinary result and how did they operate? Lamarck (1744-1829) made the first practical suggestion of a possible mechanism in his *Philosophie Zoologique*. Evolutionary changes, he said, were the result of adaptations to the environment. The giraffe got a longer neck by reaching for the leaves high up on trees and its offspring inherited the longer necks of the parents. This began a controversy, which went on throughout the nineteenth century, as to whether traits acquired during the lifetime of an individual could be passed on to offspring. The experimental and observational evidence seemed to be to the contrary. You can cut off the tails of generations of mice, as Weissman did, but you do not produce a race of tailless mice. Baby mice are still born with tails.

Why a tailless mouse, or an armless man, should produce unmutilated offspring did not become clear until later, when more was known about the mechanism of reproduction and it was realized that the germ-cells from which a new generation is formed are set apart very early in development, and what happens to the body does not directly affect them. When you chop off the tails of mice you do not mutilate the germ cells, which still have the ability to develop into an animal with a tail.

Notwithstanding the lack of experimental evidence, Lamarck's theory has had its adherents until quite recently. Some people, like Samuel Butler and Bernard Shaw, said that the biologists' way of doing the experiments was wrong. The animal had to co-operate. If it didn't *try*, the effect was not passed on. It was the effort, the urge to do things, which produced transmissible variations. This was really what Lamarck himself had believed; that an animal like a mole lost the use of its eyes not through disuse but because it did not want to use them; the giraffe got its long neck by wanting and trying to reach the higher leaves. The driving force of evolution was an urge to transcend—what Bergson called an *élan vital*—which has driven life on to create ever more varied and complex forms.

This is a difficult hypothesis to test, as we cannot measure the giraffes' efforts to reach upwards, nor can we observe any result. Nor can we examine the effort made by the trees in trying to reach the light. The scientist must ask himself, 'what is this *élan vital?*' Can it be regarded as a law of nature? If so, how does it fit in with other natural laws? If it is a law peculiar to life, the living is clearly something apart from the nonliving.

Charles Darwin found a way out of these difficulties by suggesting a way in which the evolution could take place without, apparently, invoking any unnatural force. Darwin's theory was based on the well-known fact that the individuals of a species always vary among themselves and, as breeders of plants and animals have known for many years, such variations are often transmitted to the offspring. If you breed consistently from horses which have won races, you produce breeds of faster horses; if you breed from cows with high certified yields of milk, you produce a high-yielding strain of cattle.

Darwin was aware of these facts, and he also became aware, in his voyage round the world, of the intense struggle for existence which occurs in undisturbed nature. Of the many living things which begin life only a few reach maturity, and hence any variation which gives its owner even a slight advantage will tend to be perpetuated, and new species could arise by a succession of slight variations.

It is not too much to say that Darwin's theory met with almost universal acceptance among scientists. If any theory had been searched for and desired, it was Darwin's. It exactly suited and fitted in with the prevailing ideas of the time. It was, indeed, at least partly inspired by Malthus's *Essay on Population*, which discussed the effects of the great increase of human population then taking place. It was an exact translation into biology of the Victorian ideas of competition and *laissez-faire* in economic life. It also provided for the animate world what the laws of physics did for the inanimate; namely a rational explanation based on natural effects which, working by themselves and without outside interference, would explain the evolution of species from the simple to the complex. It was immediately seen by many scientists to be the hitherto missing link in the chain of knowledge of natural causes by which the world, as we know it, has come into being.

The ground for Darwin's theory had been well prepared by unassailable evidence of the antiquity of life on earth and of a gradual increase of complexity as shown by the fossil record. Even Buffon, many years earlier, had regarded fossils as remains of life of possibly great antiquity, which he thought had been deposited in the mud of primaeval seas.

At this period the literal truth of the story of the creation given in Genesis was still accepted by many people, and Bishop Usher's calculation of the date of the creation, from the ages of the patriarchs, as 4004 B.C., was widely believed, but such a recent origin strained the credulity even of historians.

Attempts were made to explain away the fossil record. Some had been extremely naive. There was the Italian writer, who according to M. Buffon, supposed that the fossils (round Paris) were deposited on the earth at the time of the Crusades by pilgrims returning from Jerusalem, who had picked up shells on the shores of the Mediterranean and dropped them in the various places where they were found!

The churchmen did themselves great harm in adhering literally to the Biblical story of creation even when it was in conflict with the evidence of the senses, much of which was plainly evident to every man who could see and judge for himself. Later, it is true, many of them were willing to concede that the Bible story of creation was to be interpreted metaphorically and not literally, but by that time the damage was done and many people felt that if they were wrong on this issue, they were just as likely to be wrong on others. They ought to have been able to realize that

c

the new idea of creation by evolution was just as sublime as a sudden arbitrary creation, and that the scientists' universe which was beginning to appear in such vast dimensions in space and in time was itself an eloquent witness to the grandeur of the Power which had produced it.

What they especially objected to was not evolution itself, but the suggestion that evolution was the result of the action of natural forces. The attack on the evolutionary doctrine was made precisely on the ground that it lowered the dignity of man, and those who were outraged by the suggestion endeavoured to discredit the ideal by ridicule. Bishop Wilberforce asked in the *Quarterly Review*, 'Is it true that all favourable varieties of turnips are attempting to become men?' Others put forward the idea that the fossils were introduced into the rocks at the Creation—not so much, as some said, to deceive mankind (an impious notion), as to provide the earth with apparent past as well as the promise of a future.

A decisive clash between the evolutionalists and the traditionalists occurred at the British Association meeting at Oxford in 1860. Bishop Wilberforce asked T. H. Huxley, 'I beg to know, is it through your grandfather or your grandmother that you claim descent from a monkey?' to which Huxley made his famous retort: 'You say that development drives out the Creator; but you assert that God made you and yet you know that you yourself were originally a little piece of matter no bigger than the end of this gold pencil-case. I should feel it no shame to have risen from such an origin.'

Huxley returned to this argument in his Edinburgh lectures *On the relations of man and the lower animals*. 'I have endeavoured to show', he said, 'that no absolute line of demarcation . . . can be drawn between the animal world and ourselves; and I may add the expression of my belief that the attempt to draw a psychical distinction is equally futile, and even the highest faculties of feeling and of intellect begin to germinate in lower forms of life. At the same time, no one is more strongly convinced than I am of the vastness of the gulf between civilized man and the brutes; or is more certain that whether from them or not, he is assuredly not *of* them.'

It might be thought that the concept of evolution as unfolded by the scientists was so sublime that it would produce a feeling of humility and wonder in contemplating such a tremendous and potent process. But its effect on the whole has been the reverse— it gave rise in some scientists and many other people to arrogance; a feeling that because human beings could unravel such a process, they were its masters. Its political effects were immense. It was the direct ancestor of political systems which magnified brute force and regarded strife as necessary and good because it weeded out the unfit. It provided the theory behind the German cult of power politics and much of the scientific background of Marxism, and therefore must be held responsible to some extent for the disastrous conflicts of the twentieth century.

As the popular idea of evolution filtered down to the masses, man certainly lost something of his stature and dignity. He no longer appeared with a divine effulgence, 'trailing clouds of immortality', as Wordsworth put it. Huxley may have thought that he was 'from the brutes but assuredly not *of* them'; but many people were only too anxious to think and prove that the difference between man and brute was vanishingly thin.

For Darwin's theory did more than provide a *natural* cause for the evolution of the species; it suggested that the cause was just blind chance, or accident. It suggested that it was an accident which first brought together the favourable combinations of atoms in the primaeval seas, which formed the first germ of life. It was a long succession of accidents which provided the raw material of evolution by providing the variations from which selection could take place. This made man nothing more than an unusual accident in the cosmic scene—an interloper of no particular significance.

This was the picture of the world and of life which science seemed to have established, and which was very commonly held at the end of the nineteenth century. It was the corner stone of the materialistic view of man, because it suggested that the simple atoms could come together of their own accord, and, in the course of ages, under the action of purely natural forces, produce life and eventually man.

It was recognized that the chance of anything remotely resembling a primitive living unit coming together by accident was extremely remote, but it was argued that even the most remote accident might happen once; indeed, as many scientists thought, given sufficient time every possible happening *must* happen. Consider, for example, Aldous Huxley's well-known illustration of six monkeys aimlessly hitting the keys of a typewriter, who '*would be certain*, given sufficient time, to produce a Shakespeare sonnet'. The crux of the matter, of course, is the time required. In the case of the monkeys it seems to be a period stupendously greater than the whole age of the universe; which amounts to saying that such a possibility is so remote as to have no meaning at all. In fact it is found by calculation that monkeys would develop into men far more quickly than they would produce Shakespeare sonnets by chance.

The fact is that at present we know far too little of the combining powers of atoms, especially in large molecules, to make any useful estimate of the probabilities of the formation even of compounds below the level of life. We have no idea of how complex the original germ of life might be. The great weakness of Darwin's theory was that it contained no hint of how variations occurred and how they were transmitted. Of the transformations which have led from the original speck of living matter to the fantastically complex organisms of the present world, we still know very little.

So although we have much evidence that all life is one process and that, during the course of ages, evolution from the simple to the complex has occurred, and although it is well understood that the survival of the fittest is a necessary feature of evolution, we are still at a loss to know exactly what processes provide the variations from which selection is made, and especially what principle lies behind the elaboration of greater and still greater complexity of living forms as evolution advances.

It would appear that there exists in living matter a tendency to become more complex and elaborate whenever a suitable environment exists. At least we know that elaboration from simple forms to complex ones has taken place, and natural selection does not provide machinery for elaborating the more efficient forms; it is merely something which eliminates those which are unfitted to the environment. Darwin's generation could not fill this gap in the knowledge of how evolution occurs, because they had no basic knowledge of how organisms are constructed or how they grow and reproduce. Since that time a great deal has been learnt about these matters, which we shall discuss in the next two chapters.

Chapter Four

LIFE AS A CHEMICAL PHENOMENON

Biology is truly a land of unlimited possibilities. We
may expect it to give us the most surprising information and we cannot guess what answers it will return
in a few dozen years to the questions we have put to it.
They may be of a kind which will blow away the whole
of our artificial structure of hypothesis.

S. FREUD, *Beyond the Pleasure Principle*

WE HAVE SEEN how strong has been the urge to find simplicity and
uniformity in nature, not excluding living things and even human
beings. Scientists desired to bring all phenomena within a closed
circle of natural law, without recourse to the supernatural or
unpredictable at any point, and they felt instinctively, even in
advance of actual knowledge, that living phenomena must be
governed by the same laws as the rest of the universe. This faith
has been justified by a steady increase in the understanding of
living things. It led to the rejection of the idea of a special vital
principle animating living things, but the rejection was not based
on full knowledge—for no scientist could, or can now, claim more
than a limited knowledge of vital phenomena—but on a *belief* in the
uniformity of nature.

Living things are obviously made of matter, and scientists found
it difficult to believe that matter behaved differently inside a living
organism and outside. The only difference between the living and
the nonliving, they thought, was the greater complexity of the
compounds present in the former, which made their elucidation
slow and difficult. Very slow progress was made in implementing
this belief. There was a good reason for this. Chemistry lagged
behind physics, because for many years no adequate models were
found which would account for chemical behaviour.

Over a hundred years passed from Newton's time before a
suitable model (the atomic theory of Dalton) was found for even

simple chemical substances, like water and salt. Even then, and for many years afterwards, *organic* substances, as the substances present in living things were called, remained a great island of the unknown, largely outside the explored realm of natural law. It was not until the middle of the nineteenth century that models were found which were capable of accounting for simple organic compounds like alcohol and chloroform. Then a clue to the plan on which they were built was found by Kekulé and van't Hoff, in the theory of 'valency', and from that time rapid progress was made in finding the patterns in which the simple inorganic atoms are arranged in these compounds. Knowing the possible patterns gave to chemists the power to construct and create the millions of such compounds which have since been made in the laboratory. All this work had to be done before there was any prospect of elucidating the patterns of the more complex substances found in living tissues. But at least it established that, given time and patience, complex organic compounds could be built up artificially in the laboratory.

These chemical researches have only in recent years been able to approach the more characteristic substances of which living tissues are made, such as proteins, cellusose, starch, fats, and many others. Recent investigations have shown that these substances are of a complexity for which chemists were unprepared. The molecules of proteins, for example, are enormous in size and of great complexity, and much remains to be learnt about them. We still do not know how they are built up in living organisms from simple raw materials. However, notwithstanding their inability to complete the picture, chemists had no doubt that eventually their methods would account for the mechanical and chemical behaviour of living tissues, considering them purely as chemical compounds. Whether anything would then be left, which could not be accounted for in this way, they were content to leave to the future.

Newspaper reports often give people the impression that chemists are on the verge of creating life in their flasks and test tubes. These reports are very misleading. Not only is there no prospect of creating living cells, but the synthesis of many of the larger molecules present in cells is beyond the power of scientists. Even if it were possible to make such molecules, assembling them in a cell would be a task of such difficulty that we can hardly visualize it, let alone carry it out.

But notwithstanding the enormous complication of living things, much progress was made, in the earlier years of the twentieth century, in understanding the chemistry of living processes. Numerous substances were isolated which had very marked effects on various bodily functions. These were the products of the so-called ductless glands, which pour their products directly into the blood. Various abnormal conditions were traced to either underfunctioning or overfunctioning of these glands. It was found that conditions due to deficiencies could be corrected by introducing gland extracts prepared from animals, or even in some cases the synthetic compound prepared by the chemist in the laboratory. Conditions due to excess of gland function were treated by removing part of the gland or reducing its activity by chemicals.

For example, the thyroid gland produces substances which control the general metabolic activity of the body. Too much activity of this gland causes excitement, feverishness, and protuberant eyes; too little causes mental dullness. Cretinism—a state of stunted growth and incomplete mental development caused by undeveloped thyroid—can be to a great extent cured by thyroid extracts, and even by the chemical substance thyroxin.

Similarly, an excess of adrenalin, a product of the adrenal glands, leads to aggressiveness, nervousness, and depression, while a deficiency gives rise to insomnia, poor judgement, and in extreme cases various forms of neurosis.

The pituitary gland, a complex organ which lies in a bony hollow at the base of the skull, produces a variety of very potent substances. It has a controlling influence on growth, and if it is overactive in the young the result may be a giant seven or eight feet high. On the other hand, underactivity gives rise to a dwarf.

Among the many other substances produced by the pituitary gland is ACTH, which stimulates another gland, the adrenal gland, to produce cortisone, and this in its turn is capable of alleviating rheumatic diseases.

Still another example of a potent substance produced by glands is insulin, which the body requires in order to utilize sugar. The loss of the ability to produce insulin gives rise to diabetes, but diabetics will remain alive and well as long as they are supplied with insulin of animal origin.

It was also found that the sexual organs produce potent substances, which play a vital part in the sexual life. It has been known for over a hundred years that the sex glands of a cock, when transplanted into a hen, cause the development of a rudimentary cock's comb. The capon (castrated cock) usually develops only a rudimentary comb, but extract from the male sex organs of almost any species causes its full development. It was found that the substances (sex hormones) produced by these organs were necessary to produce the secondary sexual characteristics, and females could be turned into males by male gland extracts. When the sex glands are damaged or atrophied males may turn into females or *vice versa*. Maleness and femaleness thus appeared to be the result of a proper balance of sex hormones produced by the sex organs—a balance which is fairly easily disturbed.

The fact that these substances and many others—often comparatively simple in their chemical structures and easily synthesized —have such powerful effects on animal organisms, confirmed the essentially *chemical* nature of living things. It also showed that even mental processes and feelings were extremely dependent on the chemical working of the body. It suggested that even mind is a kind of byproduct of the chemical operations of the body.

Some scientists saw all behaviour as mechanical responses to stimuli of various kinds, brought about by intricate *chemical* mechanisms. The magnitude of the response depends on the glandular balance of the individual, since the glands producing physiologically active substances are more easily stimulated in some individuals than in others. This led many people to the conclusion that if man was what he was because of his glands, he was hardly to be held responsible for an overactivity of any which he could not control. Sexual feeling was hardly more than a chemical reaction—an impulse resulting from glandular stimulation.

The increasing knowledge of the chemistry of life also demonstrated the *unity* of life. So far from man being unique, his basic chemistry was the same not only as that of the higher animals, but also as that of the lowest forms of life—worms, fishes, and even micro-organisms.

All living things are found to be made of similar materials, organized in similar ways. There are apparently considerable differences, for example, between an animal and a tree, but when their basic structures are closely examined it is found that the basic cell organization is very similar. Microscopic organisms, invisible to the naked eye, are found to be essentially similar to the cells of large organisms. There is very little to distinguish the minute cells obtained from tissues of the human body from simple unicellular organisms. The larger organisms are in fact communities of enormous numbers of tiny individual cells.

This clearly supported the view that all living things belong to one family, and that the evolution from the simple to the complex is possible. There is found to be no essential change in the basic processes going on in the cells, but only an increase in the number and variety of cells united in an organism. Something is known of the operations going on in single cells, but the principles on which many cells co-operate to form a large organism are still almost unknown. A new human being, for example, is produced by the successive divisions of an original fertilized egg cell—some fifty or more—and in these divisions every organ of the body is formed. We have practically no knowledge of how this process of differentiation is controlled, how it is that some cells of the embryo develop into the liver and others into the brain, and what determines the final pattern. We see our fingers grow, very slowly, until they are complete and fully formed in every detail and proportion, but how this is brought about is still a profound mystery.

Notwithstanding this ignorance, increasing knowledge of the chemical structure and working of living material supported the mechanical view of life—now reinterpreted in terms of atoms and molecules. Life was now seen as a molecular phenomenon. 'Life could be regarded as the characteristic stable form of proteins', as J. Needham (quoting Engels) has put it. Tyndall discussed all this many years ago, in his famous Belfast address in 1874. He saw that, if life was matter, it was necessary to endow the atoms of matter with some of the attributes of life. 'Abandoning all disguise,' he said, 'the confession I feel bound to make before you is that I prolong the vision backward across the boundary of the experimental evidence and discern in matter, which we in our ignorance . . . have hitherto covered with approbrium, the promise and potency of every form and quality of life.'

Scientists sometimes think that the secret of life is almost within their grasp. When W. M. Stanley isolated crystalline viruses it appeared that at last a solution of the problem was going to be approachable. These viruses are tiny particles, much smaller than bacteria, which are associated with certain diseases like influenza, measles, and smallpox in man, and in many wilting diseases of plants. When a small quantity of the virus, even a single particle of the virus, is introduced into the host, it multiplies, and is therefore regarded as an example of a living thing. On the other hand, Stanley was able to obtain some plant viruses apparently in the form of crystals; and crystallinity had hitherto been regarded as a characteristic of quite simple substances like salt and sugar. These substances were therefore, and perhaps rightly, thought to be on the borderline between the living and the non-living. The gap between the animate and the inanimate seemed to be on the point of disappearing. One writer, for example, said at this time (1940), 'The further development of such researches may at any moment illuminate the cosmic miracle by which life may be supposed to have been produced on this or any other world.'

But further researches have only shown how complex the situation really is. For one thing, no one has ever made viruses multiply anywhere except in the presence of living material e.g. in eggs. It appears that they require and make use of the vital structures they find there. They are parasites of other living things which can only live when they can make use of part of the apparatus of life provided by living cells. They are not in themselves complete living units.

Secondly, although these particles are very tiny—in fact well beyond the limit of the optical microscope,—they are on an atomic scale, very highly organized structures. The smallest virus particle contains several million atoms, probably all arranged in a very definite pattern; and the gap between this and structures which can be elucidated by the chemist is still very large.

It appears from this work then, that the point at which 'life' begins is very indefinite. As we go downward towards simpler and smaller structures we can never find a point at which we can say, 'This is the simplest example of life.' As we go downwards from undoubted living organisms towards simpler molecules, vestiges of life and perhaps even of 'mind' will remain—though they can only with difficulty be recognized.

It will be obvious that although the 'chemical' view of living things must be quite valid, since living organisms are undoubtedly composed of matter, and scientists can hope, perhaps, given sufficient time and patience, to work out in detail the chemical structures of all the molecules present, yet in practice the task is one of colossal complexity and much remains to be done before even present methods are exhausted.

Chapter Five

THE MACHINERY OF REPRODUCTION AND EVOLUTION

EVEN WHEN we are able to explain in terms of chemistry and physics how living things are constructed and how they operate, we have still to understand how these fantastically complicated systems have come into existence. Darwin's theory was a simple one, i.e. that it all happened spontaneously, since living things are varying all the time and natural selection ensures that only those variations which are advantageous survive and eventually become dominant. This supposes that the original speck of living matter was itself capable of undergoing spontaneously all the changes which gave rise to the millions of living species, including man.

In Darwin's time the mechanism of heredity was quite unknown, but in the last hundred years a great deal has been learnt about the ways in which reproduction occurs.

All the large organisms, both animals and plants, are made of cells which have arisen from the successive divisions of one original cell. In the case of animals and most plants which have two sexes, this cell is formed by the union of a sperm cell from the male with an egg cell of a female. These two cells carry the whole inheritance of the parents, and when they unite they give rise to a fertilized egg cell from which the new individual is formed by successive cell divisions. One cell divides into two; two give four, and so on, until after many repetitions a new organism is formed. But in the course of these divisions the cells become differentiated. Some form muscles, some bone, others liver or brain.

There are two problems to be considered in understanding heredity. Firstly we should wish to know how the inherited characters are carried in the germ cells; secondly how they control the pattern of growth so that the new individual has the characteristics derived from its parents.

Now a good deal is known about the first question; but at present the second is one of the least understood chapters of science.

It has been found that cells have inside them a part called the cell nucleus, which contains the apparatus of cell division. Inside the nucleus are certain structures, which are called *chromosomes* because they can be coloured by certain stains. These are known to carry, in some way, the inherited characteristics of the organism in units which are called the genes. When a cell divides the first thing to happen is a splitting of the chromosomes into two exactly similar daughter chromosomes, then the daughter chromosomes move away from each other and as the cell divides each new cell receives one of each pair of chromosomes. So in every division of the initial fertilized egg the chromosomes divide into two sets, ensuring that every cell in the organism has its exact complement of genic material.

Now we must ask how the genic contributions from the two parents are combined. In sexual reproduction this is brought about by a simple and effective device. The ordinary body cells of the organism contain two chromosomes of each kind; one derived from the male and the other from the female parent. Of course it does not necessarily follow that all the genes carried in the two chromosomes of each kind are able to express themselves. When the two similar chromosomes carry different genes one may be dominant over the other.

Early in the life of each individual, cells are set aside which will become the germ cells of the new generation. In the formation of these the number of chromosomes is reduced to one half, i.e. to one of each kind (see Fig. 1). This is effected by a very wonderful process known as 'crossing-over' which ensures that qualities from both parents are represented in each germ cell chromosome. The two chromosomes of a kind, which you will remember come from the two parents, align themselves alongside each other and exchange parts. This is followed by a reduction process in which one half of the double chromosome is lost in some way and the other becomes the single germ cell chromosome. The result is that the chromosome of the germ cells contains a selection of genes derived from both parents, depending on which genes are retained and which are lost in the crossing-over process. When two gene cells are united in fertilization, the normal number of two of each kind of chromosome, one from each parent, is reached again.

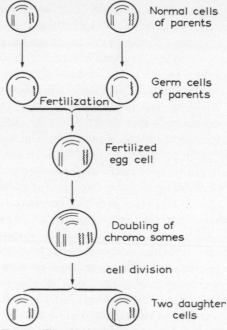

Normal cells of parents

Germ cells of parents

Fertilization

Fertilized egg cell

Doubling of chromo somes

cell division

Two daughter cells

FIG. 1. The basic processes of heredity in animals. The characteristics of both parents are transmitted to the offspring.

This extraordinary mechanism which ensures that a selection of the genes from each parent will be present in every individual, has been discovered by the work of many cytologists. It is operative in all the higher forms of life and explains the main laws of sexual inheritance which were discovered by the work of Mendel on peas.

No doubt this process is one of the major factors in evolution as it permits favourable characters drawn from many ancestors to be united in one individual. This follows from the fact that, if each individual has two parents, four grandparents, etc., going back (for example) only twelve generations each individual has over 4,000 direct ancestors and its genetical make-up is a selection of the characters from all these. Even if we allow for the fact that some of these ancestors may appear more than once in the ancestral tree, it follows that sexual reproduction is a very effective device for uniting many different characters in a single individual, and this combined with natural selection (i.e. the elimination of less favourable characters) will ensure that a combination of advantageous characters has a good chance of coming together and surviving.

But we have not really progressed very far in understanding how heredity occurs. To go further we must try to find out how the chromosomes are constructed, and what the units of inheritance (the genes) are made of, and how they function. In recent years progress has been made in this direction. The chromosomes are found to consist of proteins of a rather special kind not found elsewhere in the cells, together with a substance known as nucleic acid.* A particle of this substance has the remarkable property of being capable of dividing to form two similar particles. This is because it is made of two halves of which one is the exact complement of the other; so when the two halves are separated each is capable of completing itself, so that instead of the original particle we now have two particles identical with the original one (see Fig. 2).

The particle of nucleic acid is quite large on a molecular scale; it contains many thousands of atoms built on a repeating plan of a few chemical units (four in number). This seems to provide rather a small number of different possible combinations out of which to construct the genes. However, the role played by the protein is not yet determined, but there are many indications that the nucleic acid is the most important part of the chromosome, and it is quite probable that it will turn out that each nucleic acid particle in the chromosome is a gene. The fact that the construction of these particles is comparatively simple shows the extreme economy used in nature in producing its effects.

There are of course a large number of nucleic acid particles present in each chromosome—about 100,000 in the case of the rat. As there are about twenty chromosomes in each nucleus, this means that we have in all two million particles of nucleic acid in

---

* There are various kinds of nucleic acids. The one commonly present in chromosomes is known as deoxyribonucleic acid, which is often abbreviated to DNA.

the nucleus of every cell. Some of these may be identical with others, but there is plenty of room in the chromosomes for a large number of distinct genes. Little is known with certainty about how the genes influence the growth and form of the organism. There are indications that the nucleic acid particles act as a guide or template for the building of the many kinds of protein molecules present in every cell. But the genes do more than provide a set of

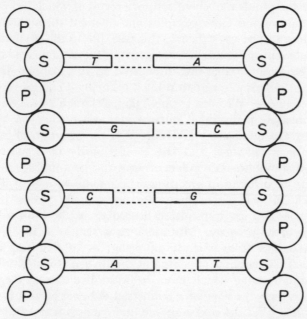

Fig. 2 A simplified model of nucleic acid according to Watson and Crick. Each side is the exact complement of the other side so that when the two halves are separated it is possible for each to reproduce the original structure. P is phosphate, S a group. A, T, C, G are compounds which are so related that A is the exact complement of T, and C of G.

patterns for the proteins required by the organism. They control details of development of the most precise kind. They cause the cells to develop into exactly co-ordinated organs, like the human hand, and the brain. How this is effected is still a great mystery, to the understanding of which very few clues have been found. The precision and beauty of the process by which new living

D

things are formed should amaze us; but its very familiarity and the profusion with which it occurs perhaps dulls the edge of our amazement. We are full of admiration of having learnt so much about these wonderful processes, but we should in all humility spare a little wonder for the processes of nature as they have been operating through many ages without our help or co-operation.

Even when we understand how inheritance occurs, we have still to solve the problem of evolution, as a result of which living things become more and more complex and efficient through the ages. According to Darwin's theory, this was due to the occurence and accumulation of favourable variations. If inheritance is brought about by genes, which are duplicated in the manner described above, an inheritable variation must occur by a change or modification of a gene. We must suppose that, although a gene duplicates itself precisely many times, a time may come when an 'error' is made by the duplicating machinery. A modification of a gene is known as a *mutation*, and the careful study of organisms has shown that mutations do in fact occur with a measurable frequency.

It has been found in breeding experiments with fruit flies that modifications of some characters occasionally occur in some individuals and are transmitted according to the known laws of genetics to its progeny. Mutations have also been recognized in human beings from a study of pedigrees of families, e.g. the disease of haemophilia appeared in the British Royal Family.

Most mutations which have been studied are deleterious in some way; e.g. the wing of a fly instead of being perfect is bent or incomplete. Yet the course of evolution shows that advantageous mutations also occur, so that we have to suppose that the gene material is capable of undergoing positive modifications which lead to the appearance of new and useful characters.

The study of inheritance therefore leads to the conclusion that the genes or units of heredity are capable of spontaneous changes, some deleterious (which are eliminated by natural selection), and some advantageous. We see the gene material gradually elaborating itself during the ages.

Our study of the chemical background of life has led us to the idea of chemical substances which have the following properties:

1. They are capable of self-reproduction.

2. In each individual they control the development of complex organization of living material.

3. They are capable of becoming modified during the course of evolution so that the gradual development of more and more complex forms of life can occur.

At present we are very far from fully understanding the chemical properties of substances which have these wonderful properties, although we may be on the verge of great discoveries. Nor do we know how nature in the first place was able to develop materials which have such a great potentiality. These properties seem to reside in the nucleic acids, and it may be that an explanation of at least some of the phenomena of life will be found in the ability of these compounds, not only to reproduce themselves (which I explained above), but also to change and develop new forms and new complexities.

When we contemplate these remarkable facts we do indeed see the possibility of an explanation of life in the many and fantastic patterns in which the inanimate atoms are capable of being combined. There seems to be no limit to the possible combinations of atoms; and living things make use of an extraordinary variety of them.

We are beginning to understand something of the principles underlying these combinations; how they operate in living systems, how they reproduce themselves and give rise to new ones, and finally how they have developed so as to give rise through the ages to always more complex forms of life.

This might seem to support a completely materialistic view of life as a chemical phenomenon, depending on the combining properties of atoms. But the converse is also true; the roots of life are traced down further into its origin among the atoms and we find it something inherent even in inorganic nature. The atoms of matter, given suitable conditions, are always trying and able to combine together into complex forms. Can we think that there is some guiding principle which, given suitable conditions, eventually leads to creatures with senses and perceptions? Perhaps there is. At last we can judge from the event, which could not be anticipated from anything we know now about atoms and their laboratory combinations. But the possibility must always have been there and have been inherent in the nature of matter itself.

So we come to see life not so much as a strange accident in the universe, a billion to one chance which just came off once, but something which follows from the nature of the inorganic world, and would be seen to be already implied and waiting to express itself in the combining powers of atoms, if only we understood them more fully.

Chapter Six

IS MAN AN AUTOMATON?

The soul, the mind, consciousness, thought, sensation, being nonmaterial, are not observable in physiological investigation like, say, nerve excitation or muscle contraction. Physiology gives no direct experimental evidence for them. Yet like all men, physiologists no doubt believe they have minds. Hence a dilemma.

M. H. PIRENNE
(*British J. of Philosophy of Science*, vol. 1, 1951).

IT IS IMPOSSIBLE to deny that the body as a whole is a physicochemical mechanism, and we must admit that many of its operations are chemically controlled. What about the brain—the controlling organ? On the one hand, it is clearly material. It is a large organ—one of the largest in the human body—and it uses, weight for weight, a greater part of our intake of food and oxygen than any other tissue. Even when we are asleep, no less than a quarter of the intake of oxygen is used in the brain. A knock on the head or a whiff of chloroform puts at least the higher centres out of action, and we become incapable of either using the senses or of performing any voluntary acts. It is quite obviously the instrument of control, in that it receives and organizes the information obtained by the senses and controls all voluntary muscular acts. On the other hand, it is also the organ of consciousness and perception. How do these fit into the scientific picture?

According to Descartes, the brain was only the instrument of liaison between the body and the soul—the latter being an immaterial something within it, which receives and judges the sense impressions and issues the orders which the brain executes. The brain itself, he thought, was mechanical. Like the body it was as mechanical as a watch. This was of course pure surmise, because there was no knowledge whatever of what went on in the brain. How it received sense impressions was equally unknown. Descartes himself described the motive power as 'like a very subtle wind, or rather, a very pure and lovely flame which is continually mounting in great abundance from the heart to the brain, flows from thence through the nerves into the muscles, and gives motion to all the members.'

It is natural that, as physical science progressed, attempts should be made to identify this force; what it seemed to be most like was the electric 'fluid' developed by electrostatic machines. This idea seemed to be confirmed when L. Galvani,* a professor of physiology and also a lecturer on the 'nervous fluid', accidentally observed the twitching of frog's legs when the spinal column was touched by a metal forceps. He jumped to the conclusion that he was witnessing an escape of the electric fluid, and concluded that 'animal electricity was secreted by the brain and travelled along the nerves.

The real identification of the messages which pass along the nerves with electrical impulses came much later when delicate instruments were available which could amplify and so detect the tiny surges of electricity which pass along the nerves. These pass in two directions: from the sense organs (such as the eye), where the physical stimulus (in this case light) is received by special cells, which, when stimulated, send a succession of electric impulses to the brain. In the same way electrical impulses originating in the brain are found to pass along the nerves to the muscles and cause them to contract. If this is so, it seems likely that what goes on in the brain is also of a mechanical or electrical nature. A delicate instrument has been invented—the electroencephalograph— which can pick up by means of electrodes placed on the outside of the skull something of the electrical activity within. It detects a continual rhythmic pulsation, a never-ceasing surging to and fro of electric currents within the brain. This is the overall picture— like the faint hum of machinery we hear on the outside of a power station—which represents the ceaseless activity within.

Many physiologists have therefore felt obliged to reject the idea that there is any separate entity—a soul or mind—existing behind the working of the brain. Everything can be explained, they say, in terms of the operation of the brain. They admit that a complete

---

* (1737-1798)

explanation of many of these operations cannot be given at present; but they claim that there is no obstacle in principle to a purely mechanical theory being adequate. If the brain can do as much as it is known to be capable of, there is no need to look any further.

They therefore regard what we call the 'mind' as a description of the functioning of the brain. In this view the physiologists have been joined by philosophers, such as the logical positivists, headed by Professor Gilbert Ryle, who find the mind equally elusive when they attempt to analyse it. They find too that mind is merely a description of some aspects of the working of the human organism.

The human alimentary canal can digest food, but no one would suggest that digestion has a real existence apart from the stomach and intestines and their working. It is merely the name of the functioning of a group of organs. In the same way, they consider that 'mind' is a name for some aspects of the functioning of the human nervous system.

We shall try to see how far the physiological description of the nervous system is capable of accounting for what we know of the behaviour of animals and human beings.

The method of science is to isolate as far as possible very simple phenomena and to find an explanation of them. For this reason scientists have tried to study very simple phenomena, like the twitching of a single muscle produced by an electrical impulse passing down an isolated nerve. It cannot really be said that at present a full explanation of even such a simple phenomenon has been achieved, but there is no doubt that a considerable amount of progress towards such an explanation has been made. At least we know something, but not a great deal, of the nature of muscles and nerves. Is what is known sufficient for a mechanical explanation of the behaviour of whole organisms?

Let us consider first of all some of the simpler ways in which actions are controlled in living things. Some actions, like the beating of the heart, go on with very little or no control from the nervous system. Even an isolated heart, from which the nerves have been cut, will go on beating when it is hung in a suitable fluid and supplied with oxygen. The beat is a rhythmic twitching of the muscles which goes on by itself as long as the organ is alive. It is nevertheless under the control of the nervous system to some extent. If I indulge in strenuous exercise so that the oxygen of the blood is used up, the heart will beat more rapidly in order to increase the rate of circulation. This kind of control is often entirely automatic—it does not involve the higher nervous system. You cannot make your heart beat faster by conscious control.

Many of the controlling mechanisms in the body are entirely automatic. They employ a principle known in engineering as 'feedback', i.e. part of the output of a process is used to control the input. For example, we can arrange to have a steady flow of water through a pipe by making its motion control the input valve; if the water is flowing too slowly the input valve is opened up a little so as to increase the speed. In the body some of these controls operate by chemical means: a chemical substance is liberated by a gland in one place which travels with the blood and stimulates action elsewhere. An example of this is the liberation of adrenalin when an animal is afraid. The brain sends urgent messages to the adrenal glands which are above the kidneys, and these liberate adrenalin, which tones up the organism, increases the heart beat, and makes the whole organism ready to receive stress. Others are nerve actions, which may or may not be under conscious control, or can be reinforced by the brain.

The first duty of these controls is to maintain the body within the limited range of conditions under which life can continue. If you get too hot, the sebacious glands release sweat which by evaporation cools you down. If you work hard so that the oxygen supply in the blood is used up, you breathe more rapidly in order to reoxygenate it, and the heart also beats more rapidly so as to bring the blood more frequently into the lungs.

It is not difficult to design simple mechanisms which work like this. For example, Dr Ashby of Gloucester has invented a machine which produces a musical note. If you change the controls so as to vary the note, the machine will always adjust itself so as to bring back the original note. He has also made an arrangement of four magnets with various switches and circuits which are operated by the movements of the magnets. He finds that they eventually find a stable position to which they tend to return when they have been displaced.

The animal also responds to changes in its surroundings, and the main object of having sense organs is to obtain useful information about surrounding objects, so that appropriate action can be taken. This sensitivity to stimuli—heat, light, chemical agents —is very deeply based in living organisms. One might even say it is a property of all living things to be sensitive to some extent to their surroundings. Many minute organisms existing in water are light sensitive, and either seek or avoid bright lights. The hydrozoan *Gonionemus* collects in the shaded regions of an illuminated tank, but *Euglena viridis* collects in the lighted regions. Loeb refused to believe that animals go towards or away from the light because they liked or disliked it, but because light brought into play an automatic mechanism which made this response inevitable. Sensitivity to chemical substances is also found among very primitive creatures. Brown *hydra* always seek regions which are rich in oxygen. In higher organisms sensitivity to chemicals appear as the senses of smell and taste and is very selective. The dung beetle can detect its food by smell over a distance of at least four metres. The whelk can detect compounds from decaying animal matter in the water, and by this means finds its way to food several yards away.

Stimuli received from the senses can cause involuntary actions, such as the blinking of the eyelid when a bright light is brought momentarily before the eye, or sudden withdrawal when the hand touches a hot surface. In these cases there is obviously a close and almost direct connection between the stimulus and the action.

Actions of these kinds—involuntary reflex actions—can easily be performed by machines, e.g. burglar alarms, which ring a bell when a door is opened, or those devices in which the interruption of a beam of light or an infra-red beam causes a door to open as you approach it. It is also possible to construct machines which respond to a stimulus in such a way as to imitate a purposive action. Dr Grey Walter's mechanical tortoises have a light-sensitive organ which is coupled with a mechanical drive, so that they will find their way to a bright light, but having found their way once they do not find it any easier next time.

It is not very difficult to construct devices of this kind in which the receipt of a stimulus produces a response. However it is obvious that in animal life the connection between the stimulus and the action is often far from direct. The response often depends on what has been learnt from previous experiences.

It was discovered by Pavlov that learnt responses to stimuli are often just as automatic as the direct and involuntary ones. He found that if he rang a bell at the same time as he offered food to dogs, they soon associated the sound of the bell with food. This was not a conscious response, as the sound of the bell was sufficient to bring about nonvoluntary responses, like salivation, alertness, running to where the food was usually found, and so on. This is a case in which a stimulus of one kind calls forth an action which is not a *direct* response, but is indirectly associated with it in a way which has been learnt. Pavlov called this type of action a *conditioned reflex*.

It is not confined to higher animals like dogs, which have a considerable power of learning. The rag worm will live in an open tube in sea water, coming to one end for food. If the worm is kept in a dim light and given food in a bright light, it soon learns to come to the end of the tube in response to light.

Pavlov's followers thought that nearly all and perhaps all actions could be regarded as *conditioned* responses to stimuli—although they were prepared to admit that the connection between the stimulus and the response might be very indirect and hard to follow. 'Conditioning' became at one time the explanation of any mental attitude. For example Aldous Huxley explained his architectural tastes in the following words: 'I was brought up in the strait and narrow way of Ruskinism; and so strict was my conditioning that it was not until I was at least twenty and had come under the influence of the aestheticians of a newer school that I could perceive the smallest beauty in St. Paul's Cathedral. Till then, its dome and round arches acted on me like a Pavlovian bell, and at the sight of them I shuddered.'

Whatever its truth, the theory that the human response to a situation depends on 'conditioning' has had enormous social consequences. Pavlovian conditioning became the official theory of behaviour in communist Russia. This was because it was necessary for Marxist theory to have a mechanical theory of human behaviour, and this was the only one available at the time. It also had the great advantage, in a dictatorship, of justifying a robot-like response of the people to the orders of the regime. Independent judgement and criticism were not wanted; all that was required was a passive obedience, hence the adoption of a theory of behaviour which makes the automatic response seem the natural and possibly the only way to act.

The most recent approach to the explanation of the working of the brain is to compare it with electric computing machines. These are wonderful contraptions which can perform most intricate calculations, and the way they work is not unlike the way the brain and nerves operate. In the computer you have conducting circuits along which electric currents pass through electronic valves. When the voltage on a valve reaches a critical value, but not until then, it allows the current to pass on to the next in the series. By this means the most complicated counting operations can be performed in a very short time.

In the nervous system, electric impulses pass along the nerves, with nerve cells or neurones taking the place of electronic valves. When the signal passing down the nerve reaches a certain strength it will cause the neurone to discharge and so pass on the signal to the next conductor; otherwise it stops the signal. Attempts have therefore been made to apply the mathematical theory of calculating machines to networks of nerve fibres, having neurones at their junctions. It has been claimed by Dr Wiener and his colleagues, the founders of the subject of 'cybernetics', which is concerned with the methods of control in living organisms, that this comparison is fundamental to an understanding of the brain, since the real function of the brain is to organize, store, and handle information, and it does this by organizing it by what we might describe as codes. From the eye, for example, a stream of impulses enters the brain and, as far as the brain is concerned, the information received is entirely contained in the pattern of these impulses. It is claimed that the laws of the storage of information are essentially the same whether in the brain or in the machine.

'We are beginning', says Dr Wiener, 'to see that such important elements as the neurones—the units of the nervous complex of our bodies—do their work under much the same conditions as vacuum tubes, their relatively small power being provided from outside by the body's circulation, and the book-keeping which is most essential to describe their functions is not one of energy. In short, the newer study of automata, whether in the machine or in the flesh, is a branch of communications engineering, and its cardinal ideas are those of the message, of the amount of disturbance or "noise", etc.'

It is certainly true that many of the operations of the brain can be paralleled by machines, such as the simple types of response to stimuli which have already been described. These are direct and immediate.

The brain also makes plans and predictions about the future. For example, it can forecast with great accuracy the result of actions like throwing a cricket ball. It not only makes the prediction, but it organizes the means, i.e. the muscular actions, which will bring about a definite result. In this it is acting like a gun predictor, which aims a gun so as to deliver a shell where a target like an aeroplane is expected to be when the shell arrives.

An animal with a brain is also capable of learning from experience. The first time an action is done, it is performed with difficulty, but after a few repetitions it becomes very easy. Also, actions which produce successful results tend to be repeated, and those which produce unpleasant results are avoided. No machine seems to have been invented which is capable of learning in this way, although one could think of mechanical ways of bringing about such a result. For example, suppose that the resistance of a conducting path diminishes with the number of times it is used; then messages will more easily follow the paths which are most frequently employed. In the same way, once a footpath has been made through a field, people will continue to walk along it even if it is not the shortest route, because the grass is beaten down.

In the same way we can suppose that, when a nerve connection is made once, and used, it is available for use again. Even simple actions involve a quite complicated pattern of connections between the controlling nerve cells. The mechanisms involved in bringing muscles into play, so as to perform an action like walking, are ill understood. Each muscle has to be operated in just the right order and to the right degree. The signals must reach their destinations at just the right times. The organization of these signals into the proper pattern involves a whole mass of connections between the nerve cells, about which little is known, but we can suppose that when these connections have been made once they are available for use again. This gives us some sort of an explanation of learning.

Are we justified then in regarding human beings as automata? How far can we regard human actions as purely automatic responses to the stimuli received from the senses? There is obviously in the brain a nervous system, much of which is mechanical (or to state it more accurately, electrical). Is this all?

The main point to be remembered is that in the above we have been dealing with very simple situations; in fact, the scientist arranges his experiments so that the situation is as simple as possible.

The 'behaviourists' tried to account for all human actions on this basis. It is doubtful, however, if this gives us a useful account of human behaviour because human actions often involve an enormous number of very involved considerations, and the situation is one in which there are usually at least two, and perhaps many more, possible actions in a given situation, and the individual has to make a choice between them. The behaviourists would say that the power of choosing is just an illusion—that the actual choice is the automatic and mechanical result of the whole situation.

We shall be able to judge this better when we have obtained a better idea of how human beings organize their information and experience.

But at least we can say now that in determining a course of action we often take an enormous number of factors into account, and our reaction is determined by knowledge, experience, and education. Under these conditions our response to a situation is determined not only by the external situation; it is determined also by personal elements in us. We make a choice in the only way open to us, by judging from what we have learnt about life. It may be we are predisposed to think in a certain way, that we have been 'conditioned' to give a certain response. We cannot help that because we do not know everything; the knowledge and experience which we have acquired as human beings is limited, but within these limits they do have an influence on what we do and to that extent we have a choice. It is no longer very useful to speak of human actions in terms of the simple reactions of a caged dog to a dinner bell. This may give us useful information about simple types of reflex actions; but it is dangerous to transfer the concepts so arrived at to the whole complex business of human living.

I shall discuss in later chapters the very complex ways in which human experience is organized, and to show how characteristic of human beings their methods of determining actions really are.

For the moment, it will be sufficient to mention some other phenomena, which are of great importance in mental life, for which no mechanical explanation can be given at present.

For example, one of the most striking features of the human brain is its ability to pick out abstract relations which it represents by symbols. It recognizes a square object as a square whatever its distance, colour, or material. How does it recognize the square-ness of otherwise dissimilar objects? The problem of how such 'universals' are apprehended has been the subject of much speculation. One suggestion, made by McCulloch and Pitts, is that the brain performs a 'scanning' operation, i.e. it examines the object at all magnifications, and the result is that features such as size and position disappear. It has not been proved that this is correct, and the mechanism still remains obscure.*

The nature of memory is also completely unknown, although some simple models have been proposed. Here again it would appear that memory occurs on a more abstract plane than the actual perception. We do not usually remember details (unless they have some significance for us), but only the broad outline. In fact we remember the interpretation we have made of what we perceive.

It will be obvious from this that the models of brain operation which have been suggested so far are of the crudest nature, and

---

* Another and more likely possibility is that the process of recognizing square-ness is not unlike the process of finding a word for an object. It involves a connection to a level of greater abstraction where the actual details such as size of the object are irrelevant. At such a level we have models of the conception of squareness, and if what we see fits one of these abstractions, we recognize the object as square. The process of recognizing a quality like squareness consists in finding a *meaning*.

scarcely touch the fringe of the problem. This does not mean that they are illegitimate, because it is of the nature of science to begin with crude models and to see if they will fit the most obvious phenomena. These efforts are often valuable because they suggest new approaches to the problem. The comparisons between the brain and the computing machines have already influenced psychiatry. It has been suggested for example that brain disorders occur when, as in a telephone exchange, the amount of traffic is greater than the equipment can carry. Anxiety neuroses are also explained as being due to circular reverberating currents, in which the 'information' continues to circulate without finding an outlet. Such ideas, though crude, may suggest new approaches.

It is unfortunate that these healthy, if rather crude, attempts to find a new approach to the study of the brain should have led journalists to call computers 'brains'. The implication is that brains are computing machines and that human beings are basically automata or robots. This idea has been publicized in thousands of newspaper articles, and has done a great deal to undermine an adequate idea of human capability. The fact that there are some resemblances should not at present be regarded as anything more than an interesting comparison. It is misleading to stress such a crude and obviously inadequate comparison, since, as J. D. Wisdom has said, 'The fact that organisms have certain properties of a machine does not establish that they have *only* these properties.'*

In their efforts to show how wonderful science is, scientific journalists often make statements and give explanations which go far beyond anything justified by the results themselves. This is due mainly to their desire to attract the attention of readers and startle them with something novel and strange. I have before me a newspaper article headed 'A Machine could Plan the Future', by that most distinguished student of the brain, Lord Adrian. The article itself gives very simply the scientist's account of what is known about the brain and perception. He speculates how greatly improved computers might be made which could remember and make plans for the future, and in fact do much that the brain does for us.

---

* See J. D. Wisdom, *British Journal of the Philosophy of Science*, vol. 2, p. 1.

He asks how we could tell that they are not as conscious as we are—whether or not they have a mind. But he concludes, 'That is something the experimental scientist is not qualified to answer. That is where the philosopher comes in. It is he who must explain the difference between the mechanical brain which the thinking man can produce, and the mind which produced the mechanical brain.'

This is a very modest conclusion and could hardly be regarded as a claim that human beings are basically automatic; yet in the newspaper the article is illustrated by a drawing of an 'automatic man'—a box full of wires and circuits, with metal arms and legs and a bright light in place of the head. One would like to know why this urge to explain human beings as crude automatons exists, if it is not just sensationalism. It seems to be the same urge which led to tales of unicorns and barnacle geese.

Chapter Seven

PICTURES IN THE MIND

And yet (and perhaps without knowing more about it)
it is not absurd to imagine that all our ideas about the
mind and its faculties will on some not far distant day
be revolutionized and transformed as at present our
ideas about the physical world are by comparison with
what they were forty years ago. What we still call
intelligence, memory, invention, genius, talent, etc.,
will perhaps appear crude notions and categories, primitive, superannuated, just as that of matter as opposed to
mind might appear today.

PAUL VALÉRY, *Reflections on the World Today*

LET US TRY to obtain a more adequate idea of the performance
of the human brain. Perhaps its most important function is to
co-ordinate and reduce to manageable dimensions the innumerable
and varied sense impressions which are received all the time by
the senses. In order to understand how human beings live, it is
necessary first of all to know how they deal with all the information
received by the senses, which is the raw material, as it were, of
living. How is it sorted out and made usable? Think of the
enormous number of sight sensations you receive in a railway
journey of 100 miles. There has to be an enormous amount of
selection and simplification. Yet we do manage to reduce them to
sense and order—in fact we extract from them what is important,
and out of this we construct a 'picture' of our journey.

When we see an object, the rays of light from it enter the eye and
are focused on the retina, where they cause sensitive cells to vibrate
and to send messages or disturbances of an electrical nature along
the nerve fibres which go to the brain. These disturbances can be
traced within the brain to regions which are known to deal with
vision, and no doubt the nerve cells which receive the messages
may relay them to many others in the intricate layers of cells which
form the cerebral cortex. There our present information about

E

what happens comes to an end, although we are aware of the result. Out of the messages we make, and in some way are aware of, a 'picture' of the outside world. What this 'awareness' consists of can be left to the next chapter. In this one I want to discuss the way in which it is used.

We are so familiar with this picture that we take it to be the outside world. We say that we are 'looking' at the objects around us. We perceive what is before us without apparent effort. The scene appears just to present itself to us. But there is no doubt that what we are aware of is really a 'construction' made from the varied sensations which reach the brain—a picture which we make by selecting and emphasizing some data and ignoring many others; a picture which, in many ways, is highly personal to us.

In certain eye operations, sight has been given to people who have been blind from birth, and they have testified to their experience of seeing for the first time. At first they see nothing but confused images—bright lights which they are unable to identify. This may be partly due to their inability to focus on definite objects; but apart from this they cannot recognize the simplest objects from their previous experience. Only slowly, by looking and feeling, do they learn to recognize objects and to pick out separate objects in the field of vision by paying special attention to the outlines. They have to learn by trial and error to make a picture of the world out of their sense impressions. Senden found, for example, that patients had to learn, slowly and with difficulty, to identify even such simple figures as triangles and squares, and this was done by carefully examining the whole figures and counting the lines and corners. It was a long time before a triangle was recognized at a glance as a triangle, irrespective of its way up or its background.

It appears from this that the recognition of patterns by the human brain is not innate, but something learnt and acquired slowly. All sorts of patterns exist in the sensations as they are received. It seems to be fairly clear that recognizing or distinguishing a pattern consists in finding some sort of meaning in the sensations. You can only distinguish a triangle if you know what a triangle is, i.e. if an arrangement of three lines to enclose space has acquired some significance for you, and this significance is a rather abstract idea which is only slowly grasped. A cat would not distinguish a triangle and a square, because such ideas have no meaning for it. The interpretation it tries to make, perhaps, is whether there is a hole or a barrier, or whether objects are still or moving.*

The use we make of the picture of the world, which we construct from our varied sense impressions, is usually a practical one. We use it to guide or plan our actions. When I walk about the room, I easily avoid bumping into anything. I am able without any effort to get from one place to another. I sit down in a chair and am not surprised to find it there. I think I am walking about the 'visible' room and sit in a 'visible' chair, but actually I am walking about in the 'picture' of the room in my mind and I sit down on the 'picture' of the chair. The picture corresponds so closely with the real world that we accept the one in place of the other, and of course the usefulness of the picture lies in its close correspondence with the outside world.

Usually, we have no difficulty in making a picture out of our sense impressions, but there are cases in which our sense impressions are ambiguous and may be interpreted in two different ways. If you look at the figures (Fig. 3 overleaf), you will see you can make two different 'pictures' from them which are equally correct interpretations of the visual impressions.

When we consider in more detail the nature of the 'picture' in

---

* The ability to distinguish in a group of varied sense impressions those features which are significant in some way, e.g. those which unite to make a 'picture' of some kind, has been recognized as a characteristic human ability in 'gestalt psychology'. For example, if you look at the crosses below you will at once see that the characteristic features of them are that they make a quadrilateral, a ring, and a triangle.

What we pick out and notice is the pattern of the whole, rather than the details. According to the strict 'gestalt' view, the appreciation of patterns is innate; but this is controverted by 'associationists' who believe that the ability to distinguish patterns is invariably learnt.

our mind, however, we see that in the human case, at any rate, it differs in many respects from a mere copy or photograph of the world. In the first place, it is greatly simplified. We select from the bewildering variety of impressions we receive, and our picture emphasizes those things which are of particular interest, and ignores many which are of no interest. Secondly, our picture of the world is greatly influenced by our previous experience. The sense impressions of the moment are modified by and in some

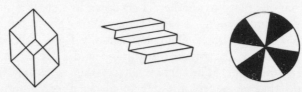

FIG. 3 Drawings which can be interpreted in two different way

way cohere with the sense impressions of the past. My actual picture is therefore a composite one made up of both the actual sense impressions of the moment and of my previous experience. It has a continuity with my own previous life. It is not merely that I recognize the room as the same one that I saw before; what happens is that the sense impressions of the moment are joined in some way with my previous 'pictures', so that the successive pictures cohere into something which has continuity and which thus provides an element of permanence in my life.

The first task in the development of an infant is to make this construction—a correspondence between his picture of the world and the world itself. In his first few months he gazes intently at bright objects and tries to touch them, feel them, suck them, and so on. He is trying to make a coherent picture of his sense impressions. He is also trying to perform satisfying actions, often very simple ones like sucking at the breast or getting an object he wants, and he is thus learning at the same time to make muscular movements. It is probably very important that the construction of the picture of the world should go on concurrently with the learning of muscular movements. Thus the child learns to make muscular movements within the framework of his picture of the world. Obviously this method of dealing with the world is only possible in a long infancy. The child is not initially 'teachable', but he can learn for himself. He has to construct his own picture of the world and to learn his own actions within it.

The picture of the world we build up is therefore not a static one; it goes along with us throughout our lives, and is constantly being added to and enlarged. The new experiences are united in some way with the previous ones to make a coherent whole. How this is achieved is not known. It is obvious that my picture at the moment involves elements which come from both the present sensation and from past sensations. It obviously involves memory and recognition. It also, as we have seen, involves a great degree of selection. This means that the human attitude to sense impressions is never a merely passive one. It involves the 'activity' of always endeavouring to interpret what one sees, of trying to make sense of it and to fit it into previous experience. It is essential for a human being at all times to try to understand and make sense of the impressions he gets from the senses.

One consequence of this is curiosity. We particularly notice elements of the picture which do not fit in or are unusual in some way. What we see has to agree with what we hear, or we will try to find out why not. We are particularly interested in what is going on at the fringes of vision and often in what lies beyond the visible. To make a coherent picture of their experiences is a deep necessity for human beings. If they are unable to do so they are unsatisfied and show signs of uneasiness and discomfort which they try to remove. The practical usefulness of this kind of curiosity is obvious.

Most of this could be said of the higher animals—at least to some extent. They undoubtedly make some sort of a picture of their world and they use this picture for their own purposes, often quite effectively in their own kind of life. They must select the important from the unimportant; they must interpret their sense impressions; they often exhibit curiosity. In so far as they make a usable interpretation of their experiences, they may be said to possess knowledge.

Yet their knowledge is obviously enormously below the simplest human level. Animals, it would seem, possess simple direct perceptions which they can interpret to the extent they need to direct their simple actions. Human beings can translate their experiences to another plane, that of symbols; and as we shall see, it is this ability which makes it possible for them to communicate with each other and share their experiences. Human beings are therefore no longer limited to whatever interpretations they can make for themselves of their own experience, for many of the interpretations are obtained from others; they have only to understand and accept them, and they can then use them for their own purposes.

In this way human knowledge has become cumulative, and from this it comes about that the all-important characteristic of human life is that it is based, not on the knowledge the individual can acquire by himself in a lifetime, or even on the knowledge a group of individuals can acquire, but on the accumulated knowledge of generations.

Chapter Eight

MIND AND MATTER

Take your dead hydrogen atoms, your dead phosphorus atoms, and all the other atoms, dead as grains of shot, of which the brain is formed. Imagine them separate and sensationless; observe them running together and forming all imaginable combinations. This, as a purely mechanical process, is seeable by the mind. But can you see, or dream, or in any way imagine, how out of that mechanical act, and from these individually dead atoms, sensation, thought, and emotion are to arise?

JOHN TYNDALL
(Belfast address to the British Association, 1874)

THE SIMPLE MODELS of brain action which I have described are totally inadequate in another respect; they do not explain how we 'perceive' or are 'aware of' the outside world. They do not even recognize the existence of this awareness, although it is probably the most important feature of human mentality. It cannot be denied that out of our various sense impressions we make a 'picture' of the world outside us. We say we 'see' what is before us, and we 'hear' sounds. These sensations may cause us to perform some action, and it is possible that there is a link or a whole series of links between the sensations and the actions. But we are also *aware* or *conscious* of the sights and sounds, and we might ask how we are to fit this consciousness into our scientific scheme. Can we find its equivalent in the processes going on in the brain? How can a collection of atoms of carbon, hydrogen, oxygen, and so forth—in whatever complex ways they are organized—be aware of anything? What is the relation of consciousness to the material apparatus of the brain?

This is obviously an extremely difficult question, because it raises all the ancient difficulties about the relations of mind and matter.

Let us approach it by considering again what goes on in the

brain while mental processes are taking place in it. Unfortunately we come up against the fact that very little detailed information is available. We are in the position of someone trying to read a difficult book, say an account of Einstein's work on relativity, without even knowing the alphabet with which it is written.

The situation is not unlike that confronting the student of physiology about 1700. He surmised that living things were made of material not very different to that of nonliving things, but he had no way of testing or even of stating this belief. It required two centuries of chemical analysis of simple substances to bring science to the point at which it was even possible to talk about the chemical nature of living matter.

The situation within the brain is rather similar. We can follow rays of light into the eye and see them impinge on the retina; we can learn how they activate the rods and cones and measure the electrical impulses which then travel along the optic nerves into the brain. To some extent these impulses can be traced within the brain. When the eye is excited by a square pattern of light, the pattern of excitement which reached the surface of the cortex still retains the shape of the original square stimulus. From these cells other waves of excitation spread out, but we can no longer identify the impulses with their origin, and it becomes impossible to trace them to their destination. The impulses are lost among the innumerable nerve fibres which connect the brain cells, and no one can tell where the 'picture' of the square which I actually perceive is formed, and what physical effects accompany it.

This difficulty of finding out in detail what goes on in the brain cells is likely to remain for a long time. This is due to the very small scale of the structures and the extreme complexity of the geography of the brain. It also arises from the fact that detailed information is required. Chemical and physical methods nearly always give information about the average behaviour or composition of cells. Something of the geography of individual cells is of course known from microscopic studies, but we should also need to know what goes on in them from instant to instant. Anything like a complete static study of the brain would be an immense task, but to follow its detailed working from second to second—even if methods were available which would tell one what was going on in all the myriads of brain cells—is all but impossible. This is the main reason why the gulf between psychology and physiology is so immense. The psychologist deals with phenomena which are fantastically complicated.

Nevertheless some progress is being made in learning the functions of isolated parts of the brain. Dr Wilder Penfield of Montreal has performed many operations on the exposed brains of patients. As there is no pain, these operations are carried on without anaesthetics and it is possible for the patients, who are fully conscious, to describe their experiences. Different accessible spots on the exposed brain are stimulated by electrodes placed on them, and the result of the stimulation is observed. It has been possible in this way to locate the parts of the brain which control the muscles of the different parts of the body. Dr Penfield describes these experiences as follows: 'When an electrode is applied to the motor convolution in the central region of the cortex, movement results in the opposite arm or leg or face. The jaw may move up or down, the throat may swallow, the mouth may open while the patient vocalizes in a long-drawn-out tone. Or the eyelids may open and the eyes turn in unison as though looking upwards and across at the opposite side. As far as the patient is concerned, these movements are irresistible. When the electrode is applied, for example, to the motor area of the right hemisphere, he cannot, by the exercise of his will, prevent his left hand from moving, but he can reach over with his other hand and thus hold the moving member still.'

Stimulation of other points produces feelings such as tingling in the hand or foot, and visual and auditory impressions. Patients reported seeing flickering lights, 'dancing lights', 'colours', 'radiating grey spots—becoming pink and blue'. Others received hallucinations or heard music. The hallucinations are often like dreams. They consist in the reproduction of some remembered experience in which 'the action goes forward as in a dream and the patient may become frightened and cry out'.

This is the clearest evidence so far obtained that mental states have a physical equivalent, and that a physical stimulus can evoke a sensation. Can we expect, then, that all our mental states will be accounted for as physical happenings in the brain? Perhaps in time we shall be able to find the physical basis of many kinds of sensations.

However, although we may find a connection between sensations and physical happenings in the brain, this does not explain what the sensation is. In fact, we are completely at a loss to describe the sensation in any physical terms. We cannot describe it as a motion of particles of matter, or a vibration, or indeed in terms of any quantities which are used in describing the behaviour of matter.

It is difficult to deal objectively with feelings and sensations because they arc absolutely personal and private to each person. There is no way in which they can be shared with other people. You cannot see what your friend sees or feel what he feels. If he tells you he has a pain you can imagine what it feels like, but there is no conceivable way in which you can feel the pain. You merely infer from his behaviour that he has feelings like your own.

My private world of perceptions and feelings is something entirely different from the outer world which I believe to exist. I can look at a scene and interpret my sense impressions of it. I see trees, houses, and perhaps people. I can analyse this picture further and notice that the trees belong to a class of things which I call plants, while the people are in many respects similar to another kind called animals. I can go further and remember that all these objects have been convincingly analysed and shown to be capable of interpretation as consisting of chemical compounds which are themselves made up of atoms. All this is my interpretation of the various perceptions present in my consciousness.

The awareness itself, the mental picture, which I am analysing and interpreting, cannot be discussed at all in any of the terms which are used to discuss and interpret the outer world. I cannot describe my perception as being made up of atoms, or even of space. It cannot be measured, it has no dimensions. The difference between my inner world and the outer world, which I infer from it, is similar to that between what is represented in a painting and what the painting is made of. When you look at a painting you find a certain meaning in the colours and shapes you see. Perhaps you see shapes which you interpret as a picture of a person and which convey to you information about that person. But this has nothing whatever to do with what the picture is made of—what pigments have been used and what is underneath the paint.

This illustration is defective in that we can, if we want to, examine the nature of the pigments and even look at the canvas. But in our mental picture there is no way of examining the pigments and looking at the canvas. We can, as I have shown, discover something about the *physical* equivalents in the brain of mental states, but there is a great gulf between the mental state (a feeling or perception) and the physical equivalent. They are incapable of being described in the same terms.

So we find ourselves in a dilemma. Must the scientific picture of the outside world stop short of mental phenomena and leave us incapable of accounting for what we know best (indeed our only direct knowledge), namely, our own perceptions and feelings? Must we accept a dual world—the outer world which is the subject of science and the inner world which is incapable even of being described in the same terms?

Some scientists have met this dilemma by denying the existence of the inner world at any rate as a subject of science. If it can never be approached scientifically, they say, we might as well ignore it— it does not exist scientifically. If the only things that we can study are the physical equivalents of sensations, these are the only matters which science can and should concern itself with. We must be content to describe the surges of impulses in the brain. For the scientist this *is* the sensation. The fact that I am *aware* of something does not concern him.

If we are not willing to ignore the inner world of perception, but think we must accept it as real—at least as real as the outer world which we have inferred—we must admit that, although consciousness cannot be described in the same terms as the 'matter' of the outside world, it is curiously associated with it and all our conscious states seem to have some physical background or equivalent. This intimate association of the two worlds (the inner world of experience and the outer world of matter) suggests that they may only be two distinct aspects of a single phenomenon.

We might, then, try to resolve the dilemma, as Tyndall did, from another point of view, by ascribing to matter the capability of sensation. This is, perhaps, less difficult to accept at the present time when the analysis of matter has led to the loss of much of its 'materiality'. The atoms of matter are no longer thought of as small hard lumps of substance, but only as complicated systems of electric forces, describable only in mathematical symbols. No doubt many of the properties of these complex systems remain to be discovered. It is perhaps not too far fetched to think that matter is not utterly incapable of consciousness, although we cannot at present put consciousness into our description of it. We cannot, for example, detect any signs of feeling or consciousness in a pound of salt, nor can we observe or study its mental qualities. If they exist they are of a most rudimentary description. Only when we study those most complicated arrangements called brains—or more precisely, the behaviour of the animals which have brains—can we see any clear evidence of mind.

The conclusion we come to is that sensations are real, although they are apparently entirely different in nature to 'matter'. But the association between matter and sensation is so intimate that we cannot avoid the conclusion that the one goes with the other. As we study the nature of the strange phenomenon called life, we find that we cannot banish feeling and sensation. Living things may from some points of view be described as mechanisms and automata, but behind the mechanical and automatic there is always something else, which in the higher organisms we describe as consciousness and feeling; in the lower ones perhaps only just glimmerings of sensation. Just as the mathematicians and physicists in the analysis of matter came, in the end, to think that their description of the material universe is more like pure thought than anything else, so in the analysis of living things, if we pursue it far enough, we find everywhere traces of feeling and sensation. This capability must be a basic property of the universe, a potentiality which existed from the start; but at present we are incapable of describing it further.

The old dualist view of things regarded men at any rate as made up of two entirely different kinds of things—*mind* and *matter*, which were able in unknown ways to influence each other. The progress of science has steadily pushed back the idea of a special vital principle in living things, as more and more extensive physicochemical explanations of living processes were arrived at, until most scientists feel now that there is no longer any need for it. Many of the researches I have described have also seemed to be banishing mind as an unnecessary concept. Yet as I have tried to show, there is something which cannot be described mechanically, and which at present is totally separate from the picture which we make of the physical universe; and we have as much right to call this a basic property as we have to regard 'matter' as the basis of everything. Instead of rejecting 'mind' as an unnecessary excrescence, we trace it downwards to the material roots of things. We find no point at which we can say, 'Here sensation and feeling begin.'

So we arrive at a new *monist* view that matter and consciousness are two aspects of one phenomenon, but we do not say that either aspect is unimportant or insignificant, or to be explained away in terms of the other. What the phenomenon is and how the two aspects are connected with each other, are still a profound mystery.

But it seems to me that the door is left just a little open, and the time may come when we can make a little progress in connecting matter and consciousness: but that time has hardly arrived yet. At least we may regard awareness and sensation—the whole world of human consciousness—not as a chimera, a mere illusion, for which there is no room in a universe of forces and atoms, but something which has a real existence. We cannot say where mind and sensation begin, because in a rudimentary way they are everywhere.

I must admit that this is an unsatisfactory and inconclusive finish to the story of the interpretation of living organisms by science, but at least it will indicate the dangers of making too simple a picture of human beings. The simple chemical-mechanical approach has the great merit that, up to a point, it works. It has certainly revealed many secrets of life; but it will be obvious, unless we shut our eyes to what is beyond the scope of present-day methods, that there are great regions of ignorance which have hardly been touched.

SCIENCE AND HUMAN SOCIETY

Chapter Nine

THE STUDY OF MANKIND

AFTER SO MANY successes with dead matter and living things, it is natural to wonder if there are any other problems to which the method of science can be applied. Could it throw any light on the principles of human society? Are there, in fact, any such principles? Is it possible to discover any laws, similar to the laws of physics, for example, by which human activities are governed? We might also ask whether human customs and ways of life, in all their bewildering variety, have any necessary basis in human nature; or are they perhaps just chance variations produced by local circumstances or by human inventiveness? Can we find anything characteristically human in all the human ways of living; and if so, how can it be defined?

It would obviously be of great interest and value to know what are the basic principles of human nature, and many attempts have been made to find such principles, even limited ones, behind human behaviour.

There are, however, serious difficulties in the application of scientific methods to human society. In the first place, the subject matter is so complex and diverse; there are so many different customs, ways of life, institutions, beliefs, ceremonies which in most cases have origins going back far beyond any record. Usually their meaning is not clearly known even to the people who practise them, and it is also quite possible for people to hold contradictory beliefs. It might seem hopeless to try to find in them any clear meaning or rules.

Nevertheless, the progress of science in other directions made an attempt to apply scientific methods to the study of society inevitable. The explorers of the sixteenth to the eighteenth centuries had brought western civilization into contact both with the ancient civilizations of the east and with savage and primitive

F

people in other parts of the world. Convinced of their own superiority, they thought of the savages they met as barely human. Even Darwin in his voyage round the world in the *Beagle* (1830) thought of the Fuegians as immensely inferior to civilized man.

'Viewing such men,' he said, 'one can hardly make oneself believe they are fellow creatures and inhabitants of the same world. It is a common subject of conjecture what pleasure in life some of the lower animals enjoy; how much more reasonably the same question might be asked about the barbarians.' Also, he says, 'I could not have believed how wide was the difference between savage and civilized man: it is greater than that between the wild and domesticated animals, in as much as in men there is a greater power of improvement.'

Later visitors to the Fuegians found that notwithstanding their harsh life (they lived practically naked in a subarctic climate) they had an extraordinarily rich vocabulary. Thomas Bridges compiled a dictionary of over 32,000 words used by one tribe.

On the other hand, the philosophers, beginning with J. J. Rousseau, thought the lot of the savage more than a little enviable. They heard tales from the South Pacific, where the islanders appeared to have a utopian existence, a life filled with bountiful ease and happiness. Many civilized people thought a little wistfully about such a life, and how nice it would be if only they could cast away all the irksome restraints of civilization and live:

> 'free as nature first made man,
> Ere the base laws of servitude began,
> When wild in the woods the noble savage ran.'

This train of thought has continued powerfully to the present day when the increasing pressure of civilization has led many to turn against it and to want to escape from the crowded life of the great cities.

Many people have suspected that, before civilization came to corrupt it, there was a golden age of human happiness, when people lived naturally and without stress and the evils which have been present in human society during all historic times did not exist—no crime, conflict, or war, no slavery and debasement of human beings. Perhaps this was a dream, but it reacted powerfully on the group of writers, like D. H. Lawrence, who preached the natural life and thought it possible to return to instinct and leave civilization, intellect, and restrictions. They were encouraged in this fantasy by the finding of little pockets of human beings here and there who had apparently retained the simple early ways of living. D. H. Lawrence saw in these a relic of the first state of human society. 'Then came the melting of the glaciers, and the world flood. The refugees from the drowned continents fled to the high places. Some degenerated naturally into cave men, neolithic and paleolithic creatures, and some retained their marvellous innate beauty and life perfection, as the South Sea Islanders, and some wandered savage in Africa. . . .'*

Actual studies of primitive life have exploded both ideas. Malinowski and many others have shown that the life of primitives is far removed from that of animals in that it is always essentially and intensely human, every act involving a whole complicated mass of ideas. On the other hand, it is far from free and not particularly noble. Savage life is full of restraints and prohibitions —though not the same as ours. On the whole the progress of civilization has been accompanied by the dropping of rules and restraints, and those that are left are supported by reason and have clearly understood functions.

But this is to anticipate the findings of students of primitive life. Until the middle of the nineteenth century there was very little actual study of primitive peoples. Darwin's theory of evolution gave an impetus to that study, because it suggested that, just as you get an idea of the evolution of species by studying existing animals at different levels of complexity, so you could trace human development by studying primitive peoples who had become, as it were, fixed in different stages of the human trek from savagery to civilization. Towards the end of the century many studies began to be made of primitive communities. This was a time when unique opportunities existed, which will never occur again, of studying tribes of people practically uninfluenced and untouched by contact with any civilization. An astonishing variety of human ways of life was discovered. Almost every conceivable way of life was being tried somewhere—almost every

---

* D. H. Lawrence, *Fantasia of the Unconscious* (Martin Secker, 1923).

possible kind of human institution and mode of association was found. Human beings were found in every stage of 'development', from the stone-age natives of Australia, with no permanent habitations, no knowledge of metals or of agriculture, and no domesticated animals except the dog, and the Eskimo leading a primitive, though difficult and highly specialized, existence round the Arctic coasts to relatively civilized peoples like the Indonesians.

All this certainly led to a greatly enlarged idea of human possibilities. Primitive peoples were certainly studied with sympathy. It became an axiom that human nature should be studied in simple communities, rather than in the complexities of civilized life. They were also studied dispassionately, without any judgement of good or bad, moral or immoral. This led to the idea that morality was purely relative and had no absolute justification or necessity, that customs quite different from one's own are not necessarily objectionable, but should be judged in their own background, and were justified if they 'worked'.

Each society was seen to have a 'culture' of its own, which embraced all the activities, 'the complex whole which includes knowledge, belief, art, morals, law, custom, and other capabilities and labels acquired by man as a member of society,' as it was defined by E. B. Tylor. Human behaviour could only be judged with reference to the 'culture' it belonged to; and the personalities of people were moulded to a great extent by the culture they lived in. 'Human nature' was therefore thought of as a product of the culture which produced it. Anthropologists began to apply to their own societies the ideas they brought back from the field. Margaret Mead could compare the upbringing of little girls from babyhood to motherhood in Samoa with growing up in the United States, and find that there was much to be said for the Samoan way of life. She says, 'Samoa's lack of difficult situations, of conflicting choice of situations in which fear or pain or anxiety are sharpened to a knife edge, will probably account for a large part of the absence of psychological maladjustment.'

'Just as a low-grade moron would not be hopelessly handicapped in Samoa, although he would be a public charge in a large American city, so individuals with a slight nervous instability would

have a much more favourable chance in Samoa than in America.'*
Western civilization was thus viewed as merely a different mode of
life, not necessarily superior.

The most important conclusion which has come out of all these
studies, however, is the recognition that human life (so far as we
have any knowledge), however primitive it is, is always distinctively
human; its primary characteristic is always that it is based mainly
on shared and communicated knowledge. Notwithstanding all
that has been written about the social life of insects and the
wonders of instinct, it remains true that human living is totally
different from other kinds of living. It is remarkable that although
the human individual has some instincts, which he shares with
animals, to assist his own life, e.g. he is wary of the unknown, is
often hostile to strangers, and has a strong affection for his own
young—his *social* life is almost instinctless. Outside the family,
the instincts we have are on the whole non-co-operative; they lead
to self-preservation and the satisfaction of individual needs. They
help to keep family groups together, but beyond that they give
us very little help.

So we see that although man has an amazingly efficient equipment for making his own decisions and pursuing his own course
of action, he has no instinctive way of combining with other
people into a society. He has been literally left to his own devices
to find out how to make a community.

This is the fundamental cause of all the difficulty of human life,
which is in some respects as acute now as ever, and human beings
have nothing but their own wits to find out how to overcome it.

Some method of cohesion has to be discovered if human beings
are to unite into any kind of society. Man is an individual and
has the ability and means of judging for himself; yet he must live
a social life, a life based on knowledge which is a communal
possession. The problem is how to reconcile individual initiative
and impulse with social cohesion. At least some accepted rules,
some sort of judgement as to what is permissible and allowed
is required. This is a judgement which no individual can make
for himself, as it involves organizing a long experience of life—

---

* Margaret Mead, *Coming of Age in Samoa*, (W. Morrow, New York and
Penguin, London).

one might say, the experience of generations of people—into a
usable knowledge. The results of this experience are to be seen
in all the human societies which exist now and the many others
which have existed in the past.

So much for the nature of the problems which human beings
have to solve in living together; now let us look at the results of
studies of primitive life everywhere. What solutions have actually
been found? The first conspicuous fact is that human beings
hardly ever live a simple life of hunting and eating or of sowing
and harvesting. Even the most primitive ways of life seem to be
regulated by theories and beliefs which go far beyond what simple
economic considerations would seem to require. Life seems to
become simple and 'economic' only in civilized and advanced
societies. Elsewhere, life seems to be regulated by a whole complex of ideas which pervade everything. It seems to be a necessity
for human beings to develop theories about themselves, their
origins, and their customs, in fact to explain themselves and their
ways of life to themselves.

The reason for this no doubt lies in the fact that human life is
necessarily more than the day-to-day discovery of the necessities
of life; it is something which must go on from one generation to
another, and the minimum organization is that of a group of
people continuing to live together at least long enough to teach
the children the basic knowledge which has been learnt from the
previous generation. Not having the guidance and compulsion
of instinctive behaviour patterns, which bring about the necessary
amount of co-operation in animal communities, primitive peoples
need concrete and definite concepts or mental pictures, by means
of which their experience of human life can be shared and communicated and passed on from one generation to another.

Everywhere we find a complicated body of tribal customs, held
together by myths which explain the customs, and supported by
rituals such as songs, dances, and ceremonies, which illustrate
them and bring them into contact with the life of the people.
The everyday life then emerges naturally from this background of
beliefs, which guide and rule every aspect of life.

Why should primitive life almost always follow a pattern of this
kind? It evidently fills some deep human need. Probably it is

because the communication of the necessary ideas can only take place in some such way. After all, what have to be communicated are not so much the *facts* of human life, as the interpretations of human experience. What the myths and the legends transmit are the human interpretations of age-long experience of life. It is not surprising that this knowledge should be transmitted in symbolic form. Human communication is always and necessarily carried on by means of symbols. Even language, the basic means of human communication, as we shall see, is entirely symbolic.

It is therefore not unnatural that the more elusive truths of human life—the framework which carries life along from one generation to another, all the results of experience which cannot easily be put into words—should be given a symbolic representation in myths and rituals. These myths may or may not be adequate to convey the facts of experience; but they are indispensable at a certain stage of human development.

As knowledge increases, they become obviously inadequate; it may be possible to replace them by logical explanations in words, which is another kind of symbolism. But the broad fact remains that, in its most complicated forms as well as in its simplest, human society is necessarily an artificial construction, and social institutions a means of uniting diverse people and of reconciling contradictory impulses, through a shared symbolism.

It is *necessary* for human beings to make such interpretations because they cannot live a human life in any other way. It is precisely the difference between the human and the animal way of life that the former is based on theories, or interpretations of the nature of life, which have usually been inherited from the past. Innumerable theories and interpretations of different aspects of human life exist. A few of the beliefs which human beings have arrived at in their attempts to interpret their experiences are described below.

It is important to notice in the first place that the interpretations of life with which we are concerned are not private and individual ones; they are necessarily *shared* by many people, or at least by a group of people living together. Now the *sharing* of experiences is not an accidental feature of human life—something which could, at a pinch, be dispensed with; it is its real basis.

We might say that man and a human way of life became possible only when there was an effective means of sharing experience and so arriving at knowledge. We shall first consider what this sharing of experience implies. We have very little knowledge of when and how human beings acquired the ability to share their experiences, and how the transition from the plane of animal life to the human way of living took place.

Chapter Ten

FIRST STEPS IN KNOWLEDGE

Language is just that needed system of symbols which
man has created for the elaboration of that new space-
time world of mind to which he was called by the 'World-
Spirit' when the world emerged from the preconscious to
the conscious cycle of its self-development.
R. A. WILSON, *The Miraculous Birth of Language*
(Dent and Guild Books)

IT SEEMS THAT men have existed on the earth in much their present
physical condition and with probably the same mental capacity
for 50,000 years or more. Certain fossil remains have been found
which may represent man in a state of transition from sub-human
types to the emergent species, *Homo sapiens*, going back perhaps
500,000 years, but practically nothing is really known of their
habits and behaviour.

We have very little information about the forces which brought
man into existence. There may have been a period, perhaps during
an ice age, when small bands of hunters followed herds of mam-
moths, when extreme quickness and skill and the ability to think
and plan had great survival value.

We can only guess at the condition of human life in those days,
but that it was not entirely barbarous and brutish is perhaps
shown by the extraordinary beauty and delicacy of the human
form as it was evolved, no doubt, by sexual selection. It does not
suggest an insensitivity to aesthetic feelings. Professor Gordon
Childe has written a book called *Man makes Himself* in which
he discusses the developing culture of the human species. But
it may be true in a much more literal sense that 'man made
himself', since the actual bodily forms of men and women have
been produced by thousands of years of sexual selection. Possibly
the human frame was more variable in those days, and conditions
existed in which effective variation could occur.

The attainment of the human physique and the human brain starts an entirely new chapter in the development of life, a new way of life based on knowledge made cumulative and transmissible.

The crucial development which brought this about was the elaboration in speech of an effective means of communication. There have been many theories of the origin of speech, and naturally there can be no certainty. All human societies we know anything about have had complex and developed languages, which obviously have a long history behind them. Otto Jespersen, in his book on the *Origin of Language*, describes the theories as follows:

1. The *bow-wow* theory, that primitive words were imitative of natural sounds, like the quacking of ducks, the barking of dogs, the splashing of water, the screeching of jays.

2. The *pooh-pooh* theory, that words are elaborations of ejaculations, called forth by circumstances, such as the deep 'Oh!' produced by astonishment.

3. The *click-click* theory (of Paget) that the motions of the tongue and mouth in making sounds are, or were, an imitation of the action represented. Thus the sound *go* is made by breathing outward, while *come* seems to imply some sort of taking in or enclosure.

4. The *yo-he-ho* theory that primitive actions were accompanied by sounds provoked by them or which seemed natural to them, like heave or jump.

Jespersen favours the idea that language grew out of natural sounds elicited by strong feeling. He points out that the more primitive a language is the more figurative it is and the greater the part played by intonation and expression. Language began, he thinks, with emotional noises uttered by human beings (and by animals)—noises expressive of exultation, sorrow, love and just good spirits. These gradually acquired conventional meanings.

Perhaps there is some truth in all these theories. The essential element in the development of speech apart from the ability to make these noises must have been an urge to communicate, and early men may well have used all the modes of expression which came easily to them in their attempts to communicate facts and feelings. There are many common words in our language to which such origins can easily be suggested.

The great urge of human beings to find meanings in their sense impressions might be illustrated, to give a modern example, by Helen Keller, who was deaf and blind from early life and yet learnt to communicate by touch. She has described, in *The Story of My Life*, her efforts at learning the meaning of signs and how she suddenly realized that things have names. She described this realization as follows:

'The morning after my teacher came she led me to her room and gave me a doll. . . . When I had played with it little while, Miss Sullivan slowly spelled into my hand the word 'd-o-l-l'. I was at once interested in this finger play and tried to imitate it. . . . Running downstairs to my mother I held up my hand and made the letters for doll. I did not know that I was spelling a word or even that words existed; I was simply making my fingers go in monkey-like imitation . . .

'One day my teacher and I walked down the path to the well-house, attracted by the fragrance of the honeysuckle with which it was covered. Someone was drawing water and my teacher placed my hand under the spout. The cool stream gushed over our hands she spelled into the other the word water, first slowly, then rapidly. Suddenly I felt a misty consciousness as of something forgotten—a thrill of returning thought; and somehow the mystery of language was revealed to me. I knew then that 'w-a-t-e-r' meant the wonderful cold something that was flowing over my hand.'

Even if we find the description perhaps a little coloured by after events, there can be no doubt about the urgency of the need of this shut-in mind to find meaning in her very restricted sense impressions.

Speech consists essentially of using articulated sounds to represent or take the place of acts and objects. No animal has this ability, and it is fundamental to human societies. Although it is so familiar and apparently easy, little is known about the nature of the transformations which are made, and the mechanism of the processes by which they are brought about. They obviously involve abstracting from the passing scene some recognizable and distinguishable elements which are then replaced by something quite different, viz. recognizable sounds and signs. But the sound is not the exact equivalent of the object or act; it is only something which takes its place for the purpose of communication. Furthermore when we consider the matter, we see that what is communicated is not the experience itself, but what it means to us. Looking at a scene, suppose I see a large mass of green, which I recognize as a tree. When I use the word tree, it is the *meaning* which I communicate—namely, my interpretation of what I see, not the actual experience.

The primary result of this communication of meaning is that the 'world pictures' of individuals are no longer quite distinct and private. When the meaning I find in my experience can be communicated to others, my interpretation can be compared with that of others, so that a 'public knowledge' is arrived at—that is, an agreed meaning which secures the assent of a group of people.

If I say, 'Look, there is a deer on the hill,' my neighbour looks, i.e. examines more intently features of his visual field, to which he had previously paid no attention, and says, '*No, it is a stone.*' I look again and try to decide if I have made a mistake or not.

It is not unusual for people to be mistaken about the meaning even of what they can plainly see, especially when for some reason they are expecting to see something else, as was demonstrated in Don Quixote's encounter with the windmills.

It is still easy for people to see in appearances what they expect to see or what they want to see or what they have been taught to see. In recent years numerous people seem to have attributed any unusual appearances in their view of the sky to the 'flying saucers' they read about in the newspapers. For example, it has been reported that two young men, who live in a suburb of Los Angeles, 'declared that, on July 25, looking up as they drove along in the car at 2.30 a.m. they saw a disc . . . light in colour, 100 feet in size. It was only about 1,000 feet up, hovering where two big brightly lit highways intersect; they thought they might track it but, of course, it followed traditional manoeuvres—suddenly dashing off.' The difficulty of accepting stories like this, which is quoted as evidence for 'flying saucers',* is that they lack the verification which comes about when the appearance can be

---

* Gerald Heard, *The Riddle of the Flying Saucers.*

examined at will and some measure of agreement reached about what is seen. A real public world picture emerges when my interpretation of what I see has to submit itself to public criticism as well as satisfy my own private ideas, wishful or otherwise.

Words imply at least some sort of classification and analysis of acts and things, and this involves picking out at least some of the salient and noticeable features. The mere fact of giving a thing a name calls attention to it, and we notice things we can name and overlook those we cannot. This is especially important in childhood, when learning the names of things is for children learning about the things themselves. Ernst Cassirer says, 'By learning to name things a child does not simply add a list of artificial signs to his previous knowledge of ready-made . . . objects. He learns rather to form the concepts of such objects, to come to terms with the objective world. Henceforth the child stands on firmer ground. His vague, uncertain, fluctuating perceptions and his dim feelings begin to assume a new shape. They may be said to crystallize round the name as a fixed centre—a focus of thought.'* Words in fact constitute the first science, and to name a thing is to be aware of its separate existence and to distinguish it as a member of a class of similar things. Science has always developed by the discovery and definition of names and symbols which describe experience.

Language, and especially written language, has another important feature; it makes transitory things permanent. *Deer on the hill* are here at one moment and gone the next; but the words snatch a permanent element from the transitoriness of existence. They do more: they give to the real world new dimensions. The fleeting world of today is enshrined in a timeless world of words in which all our yesterdays can live on. Daphnis' flute still plays as when Chloe put it 'to her mouth and blew into it as loudly as she was able, and the cows heard, and knew the note of the song, and lowing threw themselves into the sea'. They also permit the creation of imaginary worlds, since we can put words together when there are no sensations to correspond and no actions either. There will be deer on the hill when there are no deer, and is no hill. The real world thus becomes multiple: just one example, as

---

* *An essay on man* (Yale University Press).

Professor Haldane puts it, of 'possible worlds', of which mankind can create as many as it will.

There is a great danger of confusion between words and things, of not knowing what words stand for real acts and real things and what for imaginary ideas. To the primitive mind, the name was often regarded as something which belonged to the thing, a kind of emanation of it. Knowing the name of an object or a person gave one some kind of power over it. In the same way, primitives find it hard to understand how there can be a name or a word, with nothing real to correspond to it. The Greeks were also puzzled by this problem—how, for example, the word beauty could exist unless, somewhere behind appearances, there was a real ideal 'beauty' from which beautiful things acquired their character. Much of this difficulty disappears when we remember that a word is not the direct representation of anything, but a symbol of some meaning which is found in it. For example, beauty is a meaning which is found in an experience. It is nothing in itself, being only what we ourselves find.

Language is, of course, not the only method of communication. There are also ritual, music, and dancing. Perhaps these were all united in early human life, as they have been found to be in recent examples of primitive life.

Even in very early times, a highly developed art of painting existed, as the cave paintings of Lascaux and other places show. These pictures exhibit accurate observation and skill in depicting wild animals in action.

The pictures which show animals being hunted, and men disguised as animals with masks and skins, and ceremonial dances, are obviously meant to convey an important meaning, though apart from the fact that is connected with hunting, and may be hunting magic—an attempt to obtain success in hunting by representing the animal hunted—we can hardly guess what it is.

It might be argued from this that human beings were already well launched in an imaginative life—possibly an even fuller one than now, since imagination dwindles as knowledge advances. As the resources of language have increased, it has encroached on other modes of communication. But we shall see in the next chapter how primitive people explain and communicate the more abstruse truths of human life which are not easily conveyed in words.

We might ask here why an imaginative attitude to life should come so naturally and easily to human beings. It arises from the human way of handling experience. We *must* attempt to analyse our experiences and make some sense of them in order to live.

We know very little about how this ordering is managed, but it does seem to occur (and this is the peculiarity of the human mind) at several different levels of abstraction. The lowest level is a kind of reconstruction or picture of the world, something like the actual world but leaving out much of the detail. From this picture we take certain characteristic features which are replaced by symbols like words. The symbols can now be operated on, and used in place of the features of experience which they represent. The actual world is thus replaced in the mind by a symbolic world, in which all sorts of new combinations can occur.

It is the ability to create and operate such symbols which makes human life, as distinct from animal life, possible.

In the first place it makes the transmission of knowledge possible, because knowledge is both shared and accumulated in a symbolic form. The result is that human beings live in a great stream of shared knowledge, most of which they have inherited from previous generations. Individuals just participate in it for a time and perhaps add a little, but while they come and go, the stream of knowledge goes on.

Secondly it makes imagination possible and even inevitable. It is not difficult to be imaginative. It is the *reality* (i.e. a verifiable interpretation) which is hard to arrive at. One has always to choose between half a dozen possible interpretations. Interpreting one's experience *is* judging between different possible imaginative meanings for which we have suitable symbols in our minds. Everyone knows how much self-criticism is required to keep imagination under control, and how easily it runs riot. But symbols, being themselves partly imaginative, lend themselves to all sorts of imaginative combinations.

In primitive societies, and perhaps in the childhood of man, the distinction between the real and the imagination is very unclear. The real world is seen in terms of an imaginative concept, which gives sense and meaning to what is only dimly understood. The whole pattern of life, involving ritual, myth and custom, makes an imaginative unity from which all activities emerge. This will be illustrated in more detail in the next chapter.

Chapter Eleven

PRIMITIVE BELIEFS

Myth fulfils in primitive culture an indispensable function: it expresses, enhances and codifies belief; it safe-
guards and enforces morality; it vouches for the effi-
ciency of ritual and contains practical rules for the
guidance of man. Myth is then a vital ingredient of
human civilization; it is not an idle tale, but a hard-
worked active force; it is not an intellectual explanation
or an artistic imagery, but a charter of primitive faith
and moral wisdom.

B. MALINOWSKI, *Magic, Science, and Religion*

TO HAVE BELIEFS and to live according to them seems to be a
distinguishing mark of humanity. This is the remarkable outcome
of many studies of primitive peoples in every part of the world.
We are driven to the conclusion that human beings cannot live
without beliefs, at least in the more primitive stages of human life.
Whether they are necessary in modern and advanced communities
we shall discuss later.

In the first place, let us consider some examples of primitive
beliefs. They represent not only prescientific, but also prerational
attempts to organize human knowledge into a usable whole. They
are prerational because they precede any reasonable and logical
discussion of human life. They really represent knowledge of
how to live but, owing to the dependence of human beings on
nature, they take in much of the natural world as well.

They deal with human life as a whole, and in this they differ
sharply from the scientific approach to knowledge, which is, as
we have seen, analytical and piecemeal. They are theories of life,
but designed to provide a background of living. They are therefore necessarily practical and workable. But owing to the per-
sistent curiosity and imagination of human beings, they are often
more than a recipe for living; in fact, while they satisfy the human

G

need for a fairly clear picture of human beings—what they are, where they come from, what happens when they die, and how they fit in with the rest of nature—they are often expressed as myths or stories which have a compelling human interest which is still effective in arousing our sympathy.

By a curious chance of geographical isolation, it happens that until quite recently, very primitive people have remained isolated, and almost uninfluenced by civilized life, in various parts of the world. For example, when the first white people entered Australia barely 200 years ago, they found there stone-age peoples, living a most primitive kind of life, with no metal tools, no permanent habitations, no domesticated animals except the dog, and no knowledge of agriculture. It was possible here to get a glimpse of human life as it was lived in the 'long-ago'.* We shall see that, although their knowledge was limited, nevertheless these people lived a completely human type of life.

In 1894-1900 they were visited by Spencer and Gillen, who have given us a very full account of their habits and beliefs. I shall describe some of the beliefs of the Arunta tribe as an example of primitive ideas. The most remarkable thing about them is their extreme complexity and the intricate way in which they are woven into the life and customs. Clearly this is no simple life. It is already far removed from the life of any animals. Every act of an individual, and the whole tribal organization, are permeated with an intricate theory.

These people thought they originated in a far-back time called the *Alchera*, when their remote and mythical ancestors lived, roaming the country which their descendants now occupy. Everything that is sacred amongst the Arunta tribes is associated with the Alchera, and all knowledge of these times is carefully hidden from women and children. At first, they believed, there were no actual men, but only incomplete creatures, both animals and plants. Then came two beings who were described as 'made out of nothing', who lived far away in the western sky. Coming down to earth with great stone knives they took hold of the

---

* It has been denied that Australian primitives were completely uninfluenced by other cultures, as they probably had contacts with Indonesia and with Melanesia.

incomplete beings one after another and made the original human beings, who were naturally intimately related with the incomplete animals or plants they were made of. Some were thus akin to rats, some to parakeets, kangaroos, etc. This was the origin of the totem groups into which the tribes are divided in a most complicated way.

Once they had come into existence, the ancestral people started to wander across the country, lizard people taking one path, kangaroo people another, frog people another, and so on through the various totem groups.

Every one of these ancestors carried a sacred stone or wooden slate called the *Churinga*, and the spirit part of the owner was supposed to be intimately associated with this object. As they wandered over the Arunta country they made all the natural features now familiar to the natives. At certain places they halted to perform ceremonies, and when various members of the party died (or went down into the ground, as they said) the spirit parts stayed behind with the Churinga, dwelling thereafter in some tree or rock which was henceforth sacred and called the Knanja. This spirit then split into two, one half remaining in the Knanja forming a double of the original spirit, and the other half undergoing reincarnation by entering the body of a woman.

The present-day Arunta men and women are therefore re-incarnations of their spirit ancestors. When a man or woman dies, the spirit part leaves the body and flies away in the form of a little bird whose whistling is often heard when there has been a death in the camp. It goes back and regains its double at the Knanja tree, and then stays at the grave to protect the body against attacks by mischievous spirits. It remains there until the girdle of hair from the dead person has been woven. It then goes back to its Knanja tree and the spirit of the dead man returns to the grave until the final mourning ceremony is held. It then regains its double and gives rise again to a duplicate spirit which can enter the women and be reborn.

This remarkable set of beliefs covers at once the origin of man and of the tribes and the birth and death of individual human beings, and it also provides an understandable basis for the organization of the tribes into totem groups. In some parts of the world all members of a tribe or group belong to the same totem, which is thus a hereditary distinction. In Australia this may have been so originally, but in recent times the totem of the child has been chosen by the mother, and determined by the locality in which she thought the child was conceived.

The totem groups were often associated with animals, although plants and other natural phenomena like clouds were not excluded. The Arunta for example have among their totems wild duck, green cicada, dingo, emu, turkey, swan, snake, pelican, crow, and wichity grub. In one family the father may be an emu, the mother a plum tree, and the two children wichity grub and lizard. The totem system recognizes the kinship and dependence of men on the plants and animals. The individuals of each totem group are supposed to be directly connected with its totem animal or plant, and are supposed to have some control over it and in theory have first right over it, but they must only eat sparingly of it and that only when it is plentiful; certain choice bits like the tail of the kangaroo are never eaten by the kangaroo men. The totem group is supposed to look after its totem objects and perform ceremonies designed to make them multiply. They do not regard it as wrong to kill their totem plant or animal; they give permission to the other totems to do so, and in fact assist.

This organization provides the basis of the very complicated marriage laws and is also, of ·course, the background and the reason for the tribal cremonies which knit the whole complicated pattern of life into a unity.

Beliefs and customs like this have been found among primitive peoples all over the world. They possess so many similarities that the diffusionist school of Sir Grafton Elliot Smith found it difficult to believe that they could have sprung up spontaneously in different places. While there may well have been some communication of actual ideas and beliefs in the ages-long wanderings of primitive man over the face of the earth, the almost universal existence of such a background to life suggests that it fills a very deep human need and is a way of organizing experience which at least comes naturally to all human beings.

These beliefs have taken many forms, but anthropologists who have studied primitive peoples have found almost universally among them, in one form or another, a belief in a world behind the world of appearance, and in the existence of spirits of various kinds—not only spirits of people, but also spirits controlling the 'inanimate world', spirits of departed people and spirits which might interfere with human life for evil or for good. This is true even when there is no clear belief in 'gods' or superhuman beings.

These beliefs are an interpretation of the whole complex mass of human experience. Natural man cannot help being impressed by the hostility and fickleness of nature. He is exposed to calamities of every kind: famine, disease, hurricanes, and floods, whose origins are beyond his control or understanding. He has no mastery over the world in the sense that human beings have it today. He feels weak and unprotected. He is also impressed by the tremendous power of nature as shown in the sun, the wind, and the waves; the thunderclap he often regards as the voice of a god. Among the Australian aborigines even the bullroarer, which produces a noise something like thunder, was thought to be possessed by a spirit.

Secondly, all primitive people are immensely impressed by the facts of sleep and death. The contrast between a living and a dead body was so immense. At one moment you had a person; at another the visible body was still there, but it had lost what gave it life. It had lost the 'spirit' or 'soul' which escaped with the last breaths. Daisy Bates has recorded how, when a wounded man was brought to her mission, as he was brought in through the doorway, the crowd of natives 'fell on the body of the dying man and put their lips to his in a brutal eagerness to inhale the last breath.'*

Dream experiences fortified this idea of the spirit world, since it was thought that the spirit wandered abroad in dreams and was visited by the spirits of others.

The final element in primitive myths is their provision of a theory of the origin and nature of human life. As we have seen, this seems to be a human need. In order to complete their picture of the world, men appear to need a theory of human life and of themselves, to provide a reason for existence and to unite their

* *The Passing of the Aborigines*, p. 8. (John Murray).

various beliefs into a coherent whole. The social order of savages is indissolubly bound up with their myths. They do not ask, 'Is this true?' The criterion of right is coherence with the traditional view, and any deviation from this may mean disaster. Australian native life, like that in many other regions, crumbles when the tribal sanctions and organization are taken away.

Since spirits are everywhere, some perhaps benevolent, but most mischievous or evil, efforts are made to propitiate them or at least to avoid offending them. Prayers or offerings or sacrifices are made to win favours and to avert disfavour; you always have to be careful not to say or do anything which may offend them.

Innumerable examples can be offered of these practices right down to the present time. One or two will have to suffice. The Indians of South America when passing a dangerous place never fail to throw coca to the spirits in order to obtain a safe passage. The country Irish are careful not to say anything disrespectful of the 'little people' in case they should be overheard.

Important and powerful spirits (gods, or supreme beings) have to be propitiated by valuable gifts, hence the sacrifice of animals, originally even of human beings. It is often considered necessary to give to the gods the first fruits of the fields, so as to make sure that they are not overlooked, and to ensure the continued fertility. The killing of a wild animal is itself something of a sacrifice, and precautions have to be taken to propitiate its animal spirit. In some civilized communities the slaughter of animals still retains something of a ceremonial nature.

Magic practices arose from attempts to influence both people and spirits. They were based on the belief that happenings could be brought about or influenced by various 'occult' means. The means to be employed were however often based on false reasoning e.g. on the incorrect belief that like influences like (sympathetic magic) or that things influence each other permanently by contact (contagious magic). The widespread use of magic practices shows how urgent is the desire to have supernatural powers—the power to harm people and to control spirits. An enemy could be injured by making an effigy or likeness and sticking nails into it or burning it. Innumerable practices and superstitions have been based on the idea that one action will influence a similar action. Sir James

Frazer records that in Caithness one James MacDonald told how, when as a boy he went fishing with companions in Loch Aline and they had no bites for a long time, they used to make the pretence of throwing one of their fellows overboard and hauling him out of the water as if he were a fish; and after that the fish would nibble.

Contagious magic was based on the idea that things which had once been in contact continued to influence each other at a distance. It was considered dangerous to lose any part of your person, e.g. hair or nail parings, to an enemy who might injure you by damaging them. 'In Melanesia, if a man's friends get possession of an arrow which wounded him, they keep it in a damp place or in cool leaves, for then the inflammation will be trifling and will soon subside. Meanwhile the enemy who shot the arrow is hard at work to aggravate the wound by all means in his power. For this purpose he and his friends drink hot and burning juices and chew irritating leaves, for this will clearly inflame and irritate the wound.'*

Primitive people are also vitally concerned with food. They want to ensure good hunting; to maintain the fertility of the land and good crops. Propitiatory and magic practices were especially designed for these purposes. One of the chief functions of the priest-king was to ensure fertility. The Indians of South America held great festivals at the time when the fruits ripen, and dances were performed and incantations sung to speed their ripening and growth. It was often believed that sexual intercourse would encourage the fertility of the fields and either mock or real cere-monies (King and Queen of May) would be held in the fields.

Sacrifices of animals and sometimes of human beings were also made to promote fertility. Human or animal blood was sprinkled on the fields because it was believed to possess life-giving properties. Karsten records the sacrifice of a Sioux girl by the Pawnee Indians in 1837 or 1838.† She was fourteen or fifteen years old, and had been kept and well-treated for six months. She was then shot to death by arrows and then cut into small pieces and taken to the corn field. The chief then took a small piece of flesh and squeezed

---

* *The Golden Bough*, p. 41.   † *Origins of Religion*, p. 266.

a drop of blood upon the grains of corn. All the others did the same, until all the seed had been sprinkled with blood.

Supplications and offerings to the gods gave rise to priests who were specially skilled and knew the proper formulae. Magic practices led naturally to professional sorcerers and magicians who knew the secrets of magic, and possibly also, in the same category, medicine men who could conjure with sickness. Such knowledge was obviously valuable and gave its possessor such a degree of power and prestige that he became the chief—hence the many priestly kings, whose chieftainship was supported by their priestliness and by their direct access to the gods. The priest-king then became himself the vehicle of fortune and good health. It was essential for the well-being of the kingdom that he should remain well. For him to fall ill was a sign of his impotence and of the displeasure of those he supplicated, and he was killed off and replaced by another. It may happen in some cases that although the 'theory' is wrong the practice has a useful effect and might in fact have originally arisen from an observation that it did at some time produce a useful result, e.g. the practice of blood sacrifice for field fertility might have originated by noticing that spilling an animal's blood on the ground stimulates the growth of plants; and sticking pins into an effigy of the intended victim may be sound psychology, because if it comes to his knowledge it may produce intense fear. What is perhaps most significant is that these practices which were perhaps originally empirical are rationalized. Human beings need an explanation of what they do —even a false one; and their practices are usually based on theories.

In some tribes the supreme sacrifice of the king was made; but as this practice was repugnant to the monarch, the substitution of a commoner or of a prisoner was made, who was allowed royal privileges before the time came for his death. Among the Aztecs of Mexico, the handsomest and bravest prisoner of war was chosen. For a year he lived in the temple, waited on by the nobles, and treated as a prince; and as he walked about, playing ritual melodies on his flute, he was treated by the populace with the honours due to the god himself. He was given four brides known as the goddess of flowers, the goddess of young maize, the goddess of water, and the goddess of salt, who attended to his needs. On the appointed day he bade farewell to his brides and was taken in procession to the temple. Here he mounted the steps, with the eight priests who had been his attendants, breaking his flute as he did so, and at the top the priests held him over the sacrificial block and took out his heart. Immediately after the sacrifice had been completed, his successor was invested for the next year. During the last five days of the reign of the substitute monarch, the real sovereign remained in seclusion in his palace, while the court clustered around the mock sovereign.

Not only was the health of the king necessary to the prosperity of the people and the fertility of the earth, but the health of the gods also, and one of the objects of sacrifice was to give them what they needed for life and health. The Aztecs regarded the sun as the source of all life, and since they lived in fear of it losing its power, they offered it the bleeding hearts of victims, which were thrown on the sacrificial fire—the most precious offerings within their power to give. At the end of the Aztec year the priests ascended the Hill of the Star, an ancient volcanic crater in the Valley of Mexico, and waited for the hour when certain stars reached the centre of the heavens. This was taken as a sign that the world would continue. A new fire was kindled in the breast of a freshly slain victim, from which runners lit torches and carried them to the temples of every town, and from here the people carried the flames to their own homes, a sign for the continuation of life in the new year.

It was estimated by the Spanish conquerors that thousands of human sacrifices were made by the Aztecs, and one of the principal causes of their wars was to obtain a supply of victims. All this was done because it was believed to be necessary. What an example of the lengths to which human beings will go, under the influence of an incorrect theory of life and of the nature of the universe! But it also shows the all importance of beliefs, even of fantastic and inhuman beliefs, in maintaining the cycle of life.

Chapter Twelve

RELIGIONS AND PHILOSOPHIES

Rational religion is religion whose beliefs and rituals
have been re-organized with the aim of making it the
central element in a coherent ordering of life.
        A. N. WHITEHEAD, *Religion in the Making*

So MUCH for the efforts of primitive man to understand himself
and his world, and to arrive at a way of life. When we come to
civilized societies, it is natural to find the primitive beliefs elabor-
ated and refined, and built into systems of beliefs, or religions.
These are conscious efforts to make a coherent theory out of the
various elements of the primitive complex of ideas; i.e. to rationalize what the primitive had arrived at by groping and intuition and
possibly by trial and error. They must be regarded as evidence
of the pervading human urge to unite all experiences into a
coherent system, to find a theory of life which is not only satisfying,
as giving an explanation of natural phenomena, but also as
explaining the nature and purpose of human life.

It is only possible to trace here, and very briefly, one single
strand of this astonishing quest of human beings for an understanding of the nature of man and the principles of human
society. This strand is the one which led in time to western
Christian civilization, and later provided a suitable basis for the
development of science.

There were other lines of development from the primitive
complex of ideas, such as that which led to the Vedas and Upani-
shads and to the pantheistic jungle of Hinduism on the one hand;
and to Buddhism with its doctrine of abnegation, the oneness of
all life, and reincarnation, on the other.

In different places, emphasis is put on different elements of the
primitive beliefs, but nearly everywhere the belief was reached in
a supreme being or beings, who rule the world with greater or less

kindliness, severity, or attention. These supreme beings are often pictured as having human attributes, but living either in the sky or heavens, or perhaps in a spirit world—a part of the shadowy world behind appearances, which is present but intangible—from which they may watch the human world and perhaps make periodical descents into it. Human beings disregard their commands at their peril.

The gods of the Greeks, as portrayed by Homer, where they make their earliest, but not very primitive appearance, are probably ancestors who had become deified and are very much like a human family. Living on Mount Olympus, they have both the vices and virtues of mortals. Like human beings they can love and hate, and they are not above practising trickery and intrigue in order to get their way. The Greeks endowed their Gods with very human passions—frequently giving them a licence denied to humans. There is very little suggestion that the gods were guardians of morality: one took care not to offend them, and offered sacrifices to get their good will.

The Egyptian religion was a much more closely organized system of ideas—a rationalization of natural happenings, as well as a theory of human life and death. It acknowledged the dominant facts of the Egyptian world: the everpresent sun, the source of all energy, and the rising and waning of waters of the Nile, bringing life and fertility.

The sun was worshipped as Ra or Amon, the source and origin of everything. The deity of the Nile was Osiris, traditionally a good and beloved king of Egypt, who suffered a violent death but rose again and was henceforth worshipped as a deity. He was then transformed into the god of the Nile, and his death and resurrection were celebrated each year as symbolizing the fall and rise of the river.

In the Osiris myth it was claimed that he was done to death by a trick and his body scattered in many pieces; these were searched for and collected together by Isis, his sister and bride. His body was then put together again and he descended to the underworld to become the lord of eternity and ruler of the dead.

This story illustrates how a myth unites and explains natural processes and human customs. It united the idea of the return of the lifegiving waters and the quickening of the earth thereby, as shown by the germination of the grain buried in the earth, with the idea of personal immortality.

The actual physical resurrection of the body was an obsession with the Egyptians, and for this reason great care was taken to ensure its preservation until the time for resurrection arrived. Possibly this cult was a limited one which only affected the kings and high priests, and the ordinary peasants were more perishable. But within these limits it was believed that the dead would live for ever in the other world if his friends would do for his body what Isis had done for the body of Osiris. The ceremonies performed by the Egyptians over their dead kings and nobles were meant to be an exact copy of those which Horus and the other gods had performed. 'At every burial there was enacted a representation of the divine mystery which had been performed of old over Osiris, when his son, his sisters, his friends were gathered round his mangled remains and succeeded by their spells and manipulations in converting the broken body into the first mummy, which they afterwards reanimated and furnished with the means of entering on a new and individual life beyond the grave.'*

The Pharoah was supposed to be a divine reincarnation of a son of Amon-Ra. He was on earth as a representative of the sun-god in the sky, and he filled the functions both of high priest and of fertility deity. Every morning he renewed his divinity in the toilet ceremonies performed in the House of the Morning. Every thirty years he underwent a symbolic death and resurrection, like his prototype Osiris. He was the custodian of the lifegiving processes of vegetation, the guarantor of the return of the fertilizing water. Because he was immortal and a god, his body was preserved after his death with the greatest care; in fact, it would appear that the Pharoahs built pyramids for the express purpose of preserving their embalmed bodies from any possible desecration or spoliation.†

The Egyptian religion was obviously an attempt to unite, into a coherent theory, natural knowledge and the basic organization

---

* *The Golden Bough*, Chapter XXXVIII.
† See E. S. EDWARDS, *The Pyramids of Egypt* (Penguin).

of the state with speculations about human life and especially life after death.

To rid religious ideas of adventitious elements was the peculiar contribution of the Hebrews, and the Bible tells in great detail the story of their development from idolatry to pure monotheism. Their God, Jahveh, was at first a tribal god, like many others, but he was a 'jealous god', who tolerated no rivals. A rather petulant deity, he demanded undivided attention as a condition of his favours. The prophets made it sufficiently clear that he required their undivided service, in return for which he was capable of performing services. 'God forbid that we should forsake the Lord to serve other gods; for the Lord our God, he it is that brought us up and our fathers out of the land of Egypt, from the house of bondage.' But if he were disobeyed and displeased, his wrath was terrible. 'The Lord,' said Moses, 'shall smite thee with a consumption, and with a fever; and with an inflammation... The Lord will smite thee with the botch of Egypt, and with the emerods and with the scab, and with the itch, whereof thou canst not be healed. The Lord shall smite thee with madness and blindness and astonishment of heart. . . . Also every sickness and every plague . . . them will the Lord bring upon thee until thou be destroyed.'

At first a Lord of Hosts, described by Moses as a 'Man of War', who assisted and protected his people in battle, he gradually becomes a god of justice, who demanded above all righteousness. 'Bring me no more vain oblations,' He declares. 'incense is an abomination to me . . . when ye make me many prayers, I will not hear. Your hands are full of blood. Wash you, make you clean; put away the evil of your doings from before mine eyes; cease to do evil; learn to do well; seek judgement, relieve the oppressed, judge the fatherless, plead for the widow.'

The Hebrew Bible thus illustrates in great detail the gradual transformation of a bloodthirsty and jealous tribal deity into a wise and all-seeing Father of All, the universal God of all Nations. 'It is he that sitteth upon the circle of this earth and the inhabitants thereof are as grasshoppers, and stretcheth out the heavens as a curtain and spreadeth them out as a tent to dwell in . . . that bringeth the princes to nothing, that maketh the judges of the earth as vanity.' He is a being not in nature, like the sun-gods, but the omnipotent power behind nature, which existed before the creation of the world. This concept is incompatible with polytheism. In comparison, the Olympian gods of the Greeks were nothing but puny simulacrums.

The Greek gods were in fact too grotesque for the intelligent Greeks to accept, and the ridicule of the gods by Greek poets and playwrights was an important stimulus to the development of philosophical ideas. The philosophers asked, if the Gods did not rule the world, who or what did? If happenings were not entirely capricious and arbitrary, in what way were they connected? What permanent elements could be found in the changing phantas-magoria of life? If the ages-old belief in the gods and their sanction of social customs and the social order was given up, what basis for human society could be found? This led to the remarkable effort of the Greek philosophers to establish ideas of general validity and to discover for themselves the basic principles of human life.

It was an attempt to establish rules of life based on reason and argument, rather than on tradition. It involved an enquiry into the validity of reason and the meaning of words. It was these Greeks who, so far as we know, first attempted to distinguish what is true from what is untrue by reasoned argument. In other words they set up the human intellect as the judge and arbiter of truth. They questioned everything and tried to find meanings and explanations.

They were, however, much more interested in the problems of human life than in the interpretation of nature; at least that was their greatest contribution to human knowledge. Nevertheless their contributions to science were far from inconsiderable. Their studies of mathematics and geometry, although no doubt based on and derived from the practical measurements and knowledge of the Egyptians, laid the foundation of science, because they provided, as we have already seen, just that kind of abstraction from experience which made physical science possible. Their study of geometry was based on the idea that a form, such as triangle, was something real, which existed apart from actual examples of it. You could reason about such forms and discover truths about them in this way without making any actual measurements.

This was the great invention which much later made science possible, since it provided the method of scientific discovery, i.e. the replacement of the actual physical world by a model, which incorporates the essential features in a simplified form and which can be manipulated by reason. This method is, of course, not foreign to the human mind; it is, as we have seen, merely an extension of the way it deals with everyday experiences, since we pick out the important features of what we see and notice particularly shapes and outlines. The contribution of the Greek mathematicians was to reduce the picture to its barest elements; from such extreme abstractions it was possible to find out truths about shape and number without having recourse to actual objects. What they really discovered was an ability of the human brain.

Why, having got so far, did they not go further and discover the basis of modern science, e.g. the laws of motion, which had to wait another 1,600 years? The reason seems to be that although the ability to draw abstract and difficult ideas from experience was present, on the whole suitable and sufficiently simple experiences were not. The Greeks did not have the patience or much desire to study apparently trivial phenomena. They wanted to explain everything at once.

Greek science was in fact a fluid mass of hypotheses. Thales, who had learnt geometry and astronomy in Egypt, was the first to try to construct a natural cosmology. The prime substance, he thought, from which all else was made, was water. Anaximenes thought air was the primitive element, Heraclitus preferred fire. Empedocles allowed four elements; earth, fire, air, and water, and he did some experiments on the nature of air. Heraclitus believed the world to be the scene of perpetual change, in which 'nothing ever is, but everything is becoming'. Everywhere there was a tension of opposing forces. Parmenides thought everything one and indivisible. There were no opposites, but merely presence and absence: black was the absence of white. For Anaxagoras, mind was the cause of motion. Democritus believed that everything, even the soul, was composed of indivisible and indestructible atoms.

This is, of course, a very incomplete account of Greek science, but it does illustrate the confusion and inconclusiveness of it. Later philosophers turned away from it as useless. We are told by Xenophon that Socrates 'did not dispute about the nature of things as most other philosophers disputed, speculating how that which is called . . . *the world* was produced and by what necessary laws everything in the heavens is effected, but endeavoured to show that those who chose such objects of contemplation were foolish.' 'Of those who speculate on the nature of the universe,' he said, 'some imagine that all that exists is one, others that there are worlds infinite in number, some that all things are in perpetual motion, others that nothing is ever moved; some that all things are generated and decay, and others that nothing is either generated or decays.'

Socrates himself preferred to 'hold discourse from time to time on what concerned mankind, considering what was pious, what impious; what was just, what unjust; what was sanity, what insanity; what was fortitude, what cowardice, what a state and what the character of a statesman, what was the nature of government over men and the qualities of one skilled in governing them, etc.'*

This is a very clear statement that what we call natural science is unworthy of attention; but it is an equally clear statement of belief that the principles of human society can be determined by reason and argument.

The Socratic method had the most profound consequences in turning progressive thought away from the study of nature. It probably delayed the advent of science, if the times had been otherwise propitious, by hundreds of years. It was, however, a direct ancestor of the idealistic strain in Christianity.

It can be seen from this that Socrates was concerned with the definition of words and the status and validity of ideas. This led Plato to a belief in an *ideal* world behind the world of appearances. This concept came naturally to the Greeks, who in any case had a profound belief in another world. It led to the great effort of philosophers to discover what was permanent and unchanging in the world of experience.

---

* Xenophon, *Memorabilia of Socrates*, p. 5 (Everyman edition).

As we have seen, the Greek mathematicians saw in numbers and in geometrical figures something of a timeless world of relations underlying the real world. The Pythagoreans took numbers to be the very stuff of which the universe was made. The number one represented a point, two a line, three a surface, and four a solid. Out of the numbers one, two, three and four they could build a world. Since they discovered many extraordinary relations about numbers and about geometrical figures, it is not surprising that they believed that in such relations they were laying bare the foundations of the universe. These ideas anticipate Eddington's recent attempts to derive the properties of the elementary particles of matter from the consideration of pure numbers, and his belief that the universe was fundamentally a mathematical construction.

Plato went much further than this. The existence of actual horses, he said, implied the existence of the idea of a horse independently of any actual examples. Such a timeless, spaceless idea of a horse would have a perfection of which the actual horses of this world only imperfectly and transitorily partake. He had then no difficulty in believing in the existence of a world of ideas, beyond the transitory world of appearance. 'Real existence,' he said, 'colourless, formless, and intangible, visible only to the intelligence which sits at the helm of the soul and with which the family of true science is concerned, has its abode in this region.'

Plato regarded the psyche or soul as the animating principle of living things. The soul was immortal, uncreated, and indestructible. It was immortal because it was selfmoved, i.e. it did not depend on the exigences of nonliving substance. 'That which is moved by itself', he said, 'has been found to be immortal; none will hesitate to assert that this power of self-motion is implied in the very essence and definition of a soul.'*

Greek philosophy influenced Christian thought and therefore reached the mediaeval world mainly through the works of Aristotle, who summed up all the ideas and knowledge of the ancient world and was for long taken as having an authority only exceeded by that of the Bible. Aristotle's position was less extreme than that

---

* *Phaedrus* (Trans. by Wright).

of Plato. He distinguished between matter and form; but the form was not conceived as being capable of independent existence, like Plato's *ideas*. Matter had the potentiality of receiving various forms, but God was conceived as pure form and pure actuality, and therefore incapable of change. God was the first cause in the universe, because the universe must have been started and put into motion by something, which must itself be eternal and unmoved. So he arrived at the idea of God as the unmoved mover. Since thought and feeling produce motion without themselves being in motion, Aristotle therefore conceived God as being something akin to pure thought.

This was the profound conception of the ultimate power behind the universe, which the Greeks, starting from their tribal gods, arrived at in a few hundred years, and this was the form in which Greek thought was incorporated in the Christian doctrine. Because of his belief that form is inseparable from matter, Aristotle thought it worth while to study the natural world, and his works were an encyclopaedia of all the knowledge of nature which existed. He described all known natural objects and living creatures. He did not think there was any point in enquiring *why* things were as they were, since he believed that they possessed certain properties because those were their qualities with which they had been created. This stifled any discussion of the natural world.

The Christian doctrine absorbed elements from all these varying beliefs of the ancient world. It incorporated the cult of the dead and a belief in personal resurrection from the Egyptians and the idealism of the Greeks, i.e. the belief that the world of appearances does not matter, and also, in a modified form, the monotheism of the Hebrews. It took over not only Aristotle's philosophy, but his account of the natural world as well.

Considered merely as a synthesis of human knowledge, Christianity, was a great feat of abstraction and generalization, since it summed up many of the experiences and interpretations of the previous civilizations from which it drew its ideas. But it was more than a synthesis of ancient knowledge. It was an essentially new explanation of man. It inverted the old idea of sacrifice to the gods. Instead of making sacrifices and offerings to their God, Christians believed that God himself had sent His Son into the world, who by accepting death, had himself made, in this one act, a single and sufficient sacrifice to pay for all the sinful acts of mankind.

Time and familiarity has blunted for western Christendom the impact of this remarkable conception. Without going into its historical development, it may be said that, since it became the orthodox doctrine of Christianity, it created the western type of man. It signified in effect a union between mankind and the transcendental source of existence. It recognized in a sense the divine nature of human beings, as sharing to some extent in the power and permanence of God. Since it applied to all human beings, irrespective of their rank, birth, or wealth, it united them all in a special compact with each other and with God, as parts of the divine process.* The strength of Christianity lay in its universal appeal and communicability, which secured in time the adherence and, at one level or another, the understanding of almost the whole western world.

---

* I am not concerned here with the historical origin of Christianity, but only with the later attempts to systematize it and produce a coherent body of doctrine.

Chapter Thirteen

SCIENCE AND ETHICS

We are entering this century into a period requiring great readjustments. One of these is to learn once more to hold beliefs. Our own beliefs. The task is formidable, for we have been taught for centuries to hold as a belief only the residue which no doubt can conceivably assail. There is no such residue left today, and that is why the ability to believe with open eyes must once more be systematically reacquired.

M. POLANYI, *The Logic of Liberty*

IN THE LAST two chapters I have outlined some of the prescientific attempts to interpret human life and to find a rational basis for human behaviour and conduct. I now wish to ask what science has to say about these questions; whether we can expect to establish rules of conduct on the basis of scientific principles. At first sight this might not appear to present any difficulty, and many scientists think that such a basis is possible, although they are less certain about its character.

In the first place let us recall the characteristics of the scientific method which were discussed in the early chapters. In its most general form, science is an attempt to find relations between phenomena, which make them understandable and predictable. It is an attempt to reduce the number of disconnected phenomena by regarding them as examples of general laws. In physical science this method can be seen most clearly to operate by first isolating very simple phenomena, and representing them by simple models which are then capable of being handled mathematically. The actual phenomenon is thus replaced by a simplified model which behaves according to laws and principles which are clearly formulated and of which the consequences can be worked out. If the predictions deduced from the model, behaving in accordance with the laws, are successful, the model is regarded as a correct representation of the phenomenon.

It is hardly necessary to stress further the success of this method in the physical sciences. The understanding it gave of the basic phenomena of force, energy and matter, transformed human society by creating an entirely new environment for human beings.

But apart from this, as I have already pointed out, it had a great effect on the human consciousness by giving human beings a feeling of power over the rest of nature. It released the human mind from its feeling of powerlessness and inadequacy in the face of the forces of nature. The proof that many happenings in the natural world were the result of *natural* causes, which could be formulated and to a considerable extent predicted, dealt a heavy blow to superstition of every kind. It gave people confidence that the world was rational and not ruled by arbitrary powers, and this was damaging to religious authority and ultimately to secular authority as well. It eventually led, as we have seen, to the scientific study of human beings and human societies.

When we consider whether it is really possible to apply fully the method of science to human beings and to deduce principles or laws of human behaviour similar to the laws of physical science, the first point which comes to mind, as has already been pointed out to some extent, is that the scientific study of mankind is beset with very serious difficulties which are not encountered in the physical sciences. Firstly, there is the enormous complication of human life, even in the simplest societies. It is difficult, or even impossible, to isolate simple situations, as every phase of life is connected with every other phase in a pattern the origin of which can only be found in the past. The attempt to find scientific principles in such patterns of life obviously involves great difficulties. Thus some societies practice monogamy, others polygamy. Can we give any scientific criterion for preferring one or the other? The whole tendency of anthropological study has been to emphasize the purely relative character of beliefs and codes of conduct, and to discredit the idea of a universal standard of behaviour.

Secondly, as a rule experiments are not possible, so that conclusions cannot be tested by experimental variations of the 'system', to see whether it responds in the way the theory predicts.

Thirdly, and perhaps most important, it is difficult, if not impossible, for the investigator to be detached and impersonal in his judgements, as he would be if he were studying a problem in physics. His prejudices and beliefs, and in fact his attitude to life, is involved. Even if he tries to be impartial, it is possible that the whole matter may have been prejudged by assumptions which he has always taken for granted, although they may not be applicable or reasonable in the case under investigation. He may also approach the problem with a particular theory formulated and looking for evidence to support it. It is also quite possible that the very act of making observations will affect the behaviour to some extent.

So it is clear at the outset that it will be difficult to establish scientific principles about human behaviour which are necessarily true and universal and which do not contain some presuppositions. This however does not mean that it is impossible to have codes of conduct which can be justified. Indeed, as I have shown, every human society has a code of conduct and must have one in order to live and continue at all. However they have been arrived at, these codes of conduct are certainly not instinctive. They obviously have one necessary feature, that is, they are reasonably successful. They represent a kind of knowledge which is communicated from one generation to another, and it may well be that under the pressure of circumstances they are gradually modified. The question is not whether a code of human conduct is possible, but whether it can be based on scientific principles.

It might seem to be quite easy to establish some principles on which to base rules of conduct; such as the suggestion that proper rules of conduct are those which give rise to the greatest amount of human happiness, or the greatest amount of human liberty. The framers of the American Declaration of Independence regarded such principles as axioms and clearly stated them as such: 'We hold these truths to be self-evident; that all men were created equal, that they were endowed by their creator with certain inalienable rights, that among these are Life, Liberty, and the pursuit of Happiness.'

Such statements are undoubtedly codifications of human experience. They are based on what people judge to be most desirable in life. They are judgements about the kind of society which is the basis of a good life—that is, they are based on judgements of value.

The question then is whether we can establish scientifically a principle of *value*. Attempts have certainly been made to do so. For example, C. H. Waddington* suggested as a criterion of value the principle that anything which assists the general evolutionary process is to be regarded as good.

This might be tenable, although it might be very difficult to recognize which actions are likely to assist the general evolutionary process and which not. Evolution has not always proceeded from the dominant species and what seemed to be an aberration might turn out to be valuable. It might well be that the initial mutations towards humanity, although they succeeded in getting by, would not seem to be in line with a genuine evolutionary advance.

Such a principle, if it means anything practical, would obviously mean killing off, or at least preventing from producing offspring, all children and possibly adults of potential breeding capacity who have any inheritable defect, such as poor eyesight or mental deficiency. Now there are certainly people who would consider such a procedure justified and productive of good. But there are many others who would regard other principles, such as the sanctity of human life, as a higher wisdom.

How could we choose between such rival principles? They are, in fact, themselves based on particular beliefs as to what is best in the long run. They are judgements of value, no doubt based on a broad evaluation of human experience, but they are not and cannot be a scientific evaluation because the data necessary for such an evaluation are not known. Judgements of value are really an attempt at a complete summing up of human experience (as far as human beings are capable of making it), and are thus necessarily largely intuitive.

It might be said then that it is really impossible to justify such judgements, or that when made they have no real validity; but as I have suggested, human beings have to have beliefs on which to base a communal life, and they have to arrive at them as best they can.

Science isolated questions in which considerations of value were

---

* *Science and Ethics* (Allen and Unwin).

not involved. It *was* possible to arrive at an impersonal answer to them, which was equally true for all persons and which did not involve questions of right or wrong.

Science indeed at first encountered opposition because it was thought that the questions it concerned itself with were moral questions. For example, it was thought that the question whether the earth went round the sun or the sun round the earth was a moral question because, apart from the upholding of authority, it reflected on the dignity of man. Similarly, the theory of the evolution of man from the lower animals was objected to on moral grounds (and still is) because it was held to be contrary to a proper view of human nature.

It is now generally recognized that these scientific questions are not moral questions. There are clearly many questions which can be discussed, and to which to some extent an impersonal answer can be given, which do not involve human prejudices, ideals, political aspirations, or considerations of right or wrong. But the fact that some questions were wrongly thought to be moral questions does not mean that there are no moral questions.

Science is necessarily analytical. It collects information. In the human sciences it compares one custom with another. It seeks origins and reasons. It does not and cannot integrate such knowledge into a system of living, because it cannot decide what is valuable and worth while. Anthropologists may study different types of human societies, but they do it objectively. They do not seek to judge—they necessarily come as impartial observers. They may perhaps feel that some cultures are more satisfactory than others, but that is a personal predilection. To the scientist, all ways of living are of equal worth as objects of study.

Scientific study thus gives no conclusive guidance on moral questions. It is impossible to deduce from it a criterion of value, of what is right or wrong. This still has to be obtained by human beings from an estimate of their total condition, which includes what is scientifically established and much that is not. A single human being cannot do this for himself, because human wisdom is cumulative and everyone necessarily inherits the broad conclusions and beliefs which previous generations have arrived at as the basis of a common life.

Such beliefs are beyond the scope of science because it necessarily deals with fragments of experience, while a principle of value necessarily has to deal with the whole of human experience, in so far as it can be grasped. It is necessarily arrived at intuitively because it is a leap in the dark, an extrapolation from what is actually known. It is necessarily established pragmatically by trial and error; but it is more than a summation of past experience.

It might be said that any generalization of experience is a kind of knowledge, which is entitled to be regarded as science. But considerations of value really go beyond knowledge; they involve not only knowledge of what is, but a judgement of what is best, and this is necessarily a leap in the unknown and a projection into the future. To distinguish between right and wrong is not only to study mankind as it exists, but to endeavour to establish a particular sort of relation between human beings in the future. It was not an accident that the Hebrew preachers, who denounced the evil doings of the Israelites which they saw before them and called upon them to conform to an exacting code of behaviour, were called *Prophets*.

The confusion between science and morality is still prevalent. It runs for example through the works of George Bernard Shaw, who never hesitated to judge scientific questions as if they were moral ones. His approach to every question was intuitive. Every idea was judged by whether it fitted in with his moral concept of man as a responsible and free individual. Here is an example of his argument: 'Compulsion of everybody willy-nilly to dangerous blood-poisoning repeated for every virus discoverable by the new electron microscope, to sterilization, to extirpation of the rivula and tonsils, to birth delivery by the Caesarean operation, to excision of several folds of the bowel and of the entire appendix, to treatment of syphilis and malaria by doses of mercury and arsenic, iodine and quinine, all of which have been advocated by leading physicians and surgeons and some of them legally enforced today, and this without protest or even mention from the loudest champions of individual liberty of thought, speech, worship, trade (especially trade), marks the rise of an abjectly credulous worship of everything calling itself Science which goes beyond any tyranny recorded of the religious creeds of Rome, Mexico or Druidic Britain.' (*Everybody's Political What's What?*)

It is obvious that while Shaw regarded vaccination, many surgical procedures, and chemotherapy of diseases, as objectionable on moral grounds, he makes not the slightest attempt to ascertain whether they are or are not beneficial medically in a majority of cases. The scientific view is that these questions can be judged scientifically, i.e. without any appeal to moral questions of right or wrong, and most people will regard the enormous progress of medical science in the last decade as a justification of the impersonal attitude of medical science. Shaw apparently objected to these medical procedures on the moral ground that it is *wrong* to interfere in any way with the natural processes of human beings. This is certainly a possible moral belief, but it is not one which many human beings confronted with diseases are prepared to adopt. Most people accept the common view that interference with the organism is justified if it cures disease and preserves life.

A similar situation held in Marxist Russia in recent times, where the only scientific views which were acceptable were those which fitted in with Marxist ideology.* Marxist ideological concepts were treated as scientific axioms. If the scientific theories were apparently in conflict with them they were necessarily wrong. 'When he grasps Bolshevism,' said Lysenko, 'the reader will not be able to give his sympathy to metaphysics, and Mendelism definitely is pure, undisguised metaphysics.' That is, for the Marxist the interpretation of nature must conform with his interpretation of history and the class struggle. At the bottom of the Marxist system is a judgement of values, and Marxism is for this reason in conflict with the spirit of science, which attempts to isolate questions of fact from values, and to judge phenomena, without being concerned with human and ethical implications. Marxism had its origin in nineteenth-century scientific trends which are, for the most part, now superseded; although it claims to be scientific, it is really a religion. One cannot object to it on this ground—one can only decide for oneself if it is, or is not, an acceptable religion.

So having done something to clear away existing misconceptions about the scope of science, we will try to discover further what background of belief is indispensable.

---

* It is possible that this situation has changed since the death of Stalin.

Chapter Fourteen

SCIENCE AND RELIGION

FIRST, LET me recapitulate. We have seen that human ways of living are based in the first instance on the relations of human beings with each other—the way they see themselves in relation to others. These relations are based on 'values' which determine what is permissible and what not, and also what is desirable and worth while in life and what is not. I suggest that such values cannot be demonstrated *scientifically*, although they can and must be made to appear reasonable and acceptable, because they are derived from beliefs, the dimly felt as well as the known, which are an integration of human experience.

The difference between knowledge and belief, is this. Knowledge comes from the study of things as they are or have been, beliefs from an attempt to make a judgement of the many elusive and imponderable factors of human life which are not known with certainty, to bring order and value into the natural anarchy of human life.

Beliefs are therefore necessarily collective. Their whole point is social—to create a way of life goes on from one generation to another.

A pervading background of shared beliefs is a necessity if human beings are to cohere into a society, and the nature of the beliefs determines the kind of society and the kind of individual lives which people live. Such a framework of belief or theory is an inescapable circumstance of human life, because human beings *must* organize their impressions into a system in order to make them manageable and to give direction to life. It is the only way they can organize the complex and elusive experiences and judgements of life into a manageable form. This is the basic requirement of human existence—the alternative is anarchy and chaos and as a consequence nonsurvival.

It has been the function of religion to provide such a theory—

a background of shared beliefs from which individually and socially valuable actions can emerge giving life meaning and significance. But the religious pattern is much more than a practical prescription for maintaining a way of life. It also maintains and illustrates the judgements of value which are involved. It has produced the great human myths which in a thousand forms have been an inspiration to human beings because they illustrate the central and pregnant situations in which humanity finds itself. They give human beings a set of patterns of human relations or, using the word in an unhackneyed sense, ideals. The myth, says Hans Schaar,* 'voices the aspirations, the struggles, and also the horror and terror that are inevitably bound up with human existence.' It is 'never a matter of caprice, of the desire for amusement, or of make-believe with an illusory world that marks the grimness of reality . . . it is always a way of expressing profoundly human experiences.'

We may or may not accept Jung's contention that myths are projections of entities present in the unconscious inner world, but there can be little doubt that they are expressions of some dimly understood aspects of the collective mind, collective because all human concepts are necessarily shared. Many myths appear to be the expression of collective beliefs which probably go back to archaic humanity, and there can be no doubt of their deep significance as expressing human truths which cannot be otherwise expressed.†

But in addition to containing and systematizing such truths about humanity, religions have to a greater or less degree, and in innumerable ways, expressed the human feeling of awe at the majesty of nature and wonder about human existence. Nearly all religions have recognized the existence of a power or potency, by whatever name it is known, which, though it may include human beings in its operations, also in some ways manifestly excludes them. It is to be worshipped, to be feared, propitiated, and even humoured. It has appeared and been responded to in

---

* Hans Schaar, *Religion and the cure of souls in Jung's Psychology.*

† I do not think that human beings have in themselves any memory of what happened in previous generations. The concepts which may have come from primitive times are in the shared knowledge of the community, which is communicated afresh to each individual.

many different ways, but it is probably safe to say that all human beings have been aware of it in one way or another.

The primitive religions tried to propitiate the powers of the unseen world and to secure their assistance, or at least to avoid their displeasure. These powers or spirits appeared to be distinctly inhuman. The central effort of the developed religions has been to find a way of relating individual men and their actions and aspirations to the hidden source of power in the universe—in fact, to mediate between God and man. On the one hand they necessarily saw men as sharing at least to some extent in the universal power; on the other, human duties and needs appeared as a reflection of divine nature and command.

Religions are often centred round death and the disposal of the dead. The fact of death obviously made a deep impression on primitive man and perhaps was the source of all religious observations. The idea of survival after death in one form or another is very widespread among primitive peoples. This is not difficult to understand when one considers the almost universal primitive belief in the existence of an unseen world behind appearances. To them the death of a person meant merely his withdrawal into the unseen world. These beliefs probably spring from the nature of the human 'vision' in which, as I have shown, imagination plays a part and, in primitive times, a much greater part than now.

It is natural that religious beliefs should not be capable of strict proof, although they must be capable of being justified and of being made acceptable to everyone. Most religions realize this and put emphasis on the necessity of faith and on the justification of belief by results. To be useful as a guide to life they must give a fairly clear lead on the practical problems of life.

The tendency of all doctrinal systems to elaboration led them to incorporate as much as they could of the knowledge and speculation of their time, and in so far as they included speculations on concrete matters they are vulnerable to the advance of science. Christianity was particularly vulnerable because of its completeness as a system of knowledge. But the real force of the scientific attack on religion comes not from details of doctrines which have had to be given up (though the vulnerability of religious doctrine on minor points led to a damaging loss of credit), but from the great extension of the scope of natural law in the universe. The ordinary everyday happenings in the world were shown to be due to the automatic operation of understandable laws. It appeared to be a reasonable inference from scientific knowledge, incomplete as it was, that the power behind the universe, whatever its nature, did not interfere in day-to-day events. It was something remote and unfathomable, and there seemed no reason to expect that it had any direct influence on happenings in our world, human or inhuman. So far as human behaviour was concerned it was neutral, like Thomas Hardy's *Immanent Will*, which

> 'has woven with an absent heed
> Since life first was; and ever will so weave.'

There was no point in worshipping or propitiating anything so indifferent.

The central religious belief in the existence of 'another world' and the survival of the human spirit after bodily death has also become vulnerable. The increase of the knowledge of the physiology of the human body has shown the utter dependence of all human functions, including mental ones, on the material machine, and it has become increasingly difficult to see how there could be any survival of human personality after the dissolution of the body. The whole tendency of modern science is to discredit any dualist position and to deny the possibility of any residue surviving apart from its material substratum.

There is no very effective answer to these arguments. But there are other and perhaps more profound considerations. After all, the scientific picture is not, and cannot be, complete. There are questions to which no scientific answer can be given. We are always in the presence of insoluble mysteries, to which science is unable to give an answer. It may have lifted a veil on the nature of the universe, but only to reveal a stupendous spectacle which seems to dwarf all human considerations, leaving human beings without a clue as to why and wherefore, and what their place is. The universe, even as we know it now, clearly transcends all human considerations. It existed for long ages when there were no human beings to try to understand it. We get glimpses of a tremendous process of which we are part and in which we try to find law and meaning. We have been very successful in this effort; there is no doubt that this universe is a scene of natural laws. But behind such questions are the questions of significance of the whole process, of the meaning of existence. This situation is not a temporary circumstance arising from the present state of know-ledge, but a permanent state of affairs which is inherent in the human situation.

The scientist will probably reply that such questions as the meaning of existence are not real questions, because they have no scientific answers, that speculations about what is unknowable cannot help us very much, and that we had better adopt an agnostic attitude about what cannot be known.

Yet I have tried to show that human beings do need to make judgements about their total situation. They can no doubt get along without knowing the origin and destination of the universe, but they must make some judgement of the nature of man, and such a judgement must also to some extent go beyond what is definitely known. It is not *unreasonable* for human beings to sense that there are faculties, in or behind the universe, which are at least not foreign to human faculties; that human perception and feeling is not a totally isolated phenomenon; that the universe as a whole is not *less* than its parts. These feelings cannot be treated scientifically, at least not at present, but they are none the less legitimate. It may be that in the future we shall get glimpses of truths which now elude us, that science will delve more deeply into the underlying substratum of things and arrive at a synthesis which includes mind and matter. But human beings cannot wait for a perfecting of knowledge, they have to live now; and even when greater knowledge is obtained, it may turn out to be equally inadequate as a basis of personal life and of human society.

The real justification for beliefs is that it is profoundly necessary for human beings to find meaning in their experiences. One might say that any theory, provided it is broadly based and fervently held, is better than no theory; certainly many theories of life have been held in different communities and have been efficacious in human societies. One might ask, what is the minimum of belief on which human society can be based? Could we not, for example, build up a practical ethical code, based on the accumulated wisdom of mankind, by a code based on what is called a scientific humanism It might be said that such a code exists already, and is acceptable, at least in principle, by a large part of mankind. It is really the ethics of Christianity without the dogmas. There is no doubt that, whatever is the fate of Christian dogma, the practical ethics arising from it have had a profound effect on mankind.

But an ethical code, however strongly it appeals to thinking people, leaves the imagination untouched. Ordinary human beings need, or at any rate respond to, something more poetic and resonating. The problem is not an individual one but the question of how to inspire masses of people with a pattern of thought and a way of looking at human experience. It also requires an unshakable conviction of its necessity.

Christianity did this for many centuries for the western world. It appealed both to the heart and to the mind. While it was a crystallization of all the main lines of thought of the ancient world, it was also something new and distinctive in its emphasis on simple human relations and on human personality. It was this emphasis which has given western civilization its distinctive character. In due course its humility, its ethics, its concern for the individual, gave rise to the principles of individualism, liberty, and the rights of man, which are basic to western European civilization and which have spread through much of the world. It provided the seedbed, out of which came that tremendous outburst of European creativity in art, literature, and science, which has transformed the world, and which all other civilizations are at present endeavouring to assimilate, on their own terms.

I am well aware that this account of Christianity will not appeal to those who accept it as a revealed religion. But I am writing primarily for the many who not only no longer accept the complete Christian dogma and also doubt the necessity of having any beliefs. I am asking them to consider again whether beliefs are still necessary; and if they do not, in fact, hold beliefs which are derived from and which are part and parcel of the Christian background of western civilization. I hope I have shown that: (1) science itself does not provide a sufficient knowledge of human nature to determine all the relations of human beings; (2) human relations and human societies are in fact based on beliefs which cannot be scientifically proven; (3) beliefs are essential as a guide to living.

It will be clear that science and religion do not occupy the same region; and they are not necessarily in conflict—in fact one might say that whatever is the subject of science cannot belong to religion. Religion is necessarily concerned with what is not known scientifically. Its real object is not so much human behaviour as human aspirations; it deals not with what human beings do and how, but with what they ought to do and why. It is an attempt to chart a course into the uncertain future; to create new human beings. It deals with all the imponderables of the human situation. It is necessarily based on faith, as the religions have always claimed. It is a passionate attempt to create a kind of man and a kind of society. It should not deny what is known and clearly demonstrated, but it must always go beyond certain knowledge.

As we have seen, science operates by breaking up experience into easily manageable fragments; but religion deals with the only partly apprehended whole. In the last three hundred years the progress of science has resulted in a fragmentation of knowledge into a series of compartments, each of which can only be appreciated and understood by experts. This fragmentation has intruded itself into every aspect of life, and as a result we are suspicious of all-embracing views of any kind. Limited horizons in every field of activity, in politics as well as science, are thought sufficient; a man should not concern himself with matters he does not have expert knowledge of. As a result the common ground held by people of different occupations has narrowed, and society tends to break up into hostile and competitive groups. Such common ground as still exists comes from the past, and even that is far from being firmly held. Hence western societies do not believe profoundly in their own aims; they are unsure of themselves, since they do not know what to believe or what objectives to aim at.

What is needed is a new integration of knowledge and belief— which will assimilate all the detailed knowledge of the scientific epoch and will incorporate it into a living faith which will again give people a feeling of wholeness. Perhaps it is too soon for this to happen; and it may be that western life will have to be eroded to its roots before it can be rebuilt.

I

Chapter Fifteen

HUMAN NATURE

Science in her perpetual incompleteness and insufficiency
is driven to hope for her salvation in new discoveries and
new ways of regarding things. She does well, in order
not to be deceived, to arm herself with scepticism and
to accept nothing new unless it has withstood the
strictest examination.

S. FREUD, *Collected Papers*

IN THE PREVIOUS CHAPTERS I have tried to show how human
knowledge comes from our efforts to analyse experiences and to
make sense of them. This kind of effort is inescapable for human
beings because they cannot live without reducing their sense
impressions to some sort of order, at least sufficient for the
business of living. Very little is known about how this ordering of
experience is managed—but we do know that the first result is a
kind of reconstruction of the outside world. Beyond this, in
dealing with the more elusive aspects of human relations and
living, our minds operate mainly by means of symbols. I have
endeavoured to show that human achievements have come about
as a consequence of this human way of dealing with experiences.
Human ways of living are thus a direct result of the way our
minds work, that is, how we deal with experiences.

This method consists of a process of abstraction which goes on
at several different levels. From the actual sense impressions we
abstract images (which I have called 'pictures on the mind'); from
images we take characteristic features which we replace by symbols.
Symbols can be further organized into a coherent system of
knowledge and beliefs.

It is this method of dealing with experience by successive
abstractions which gives human beings their peculiar abilities and
distinguishes human life from animal life. The actual experienced
world is replaced by a symbolic world, and human knowledge has

arisen because when the actual world is replaced by symbols it is much easier to discover relationships between different experiences. The discovery of a symbol (like a word) to represent some aspect of experience is itself a kind of knowledge. It means recognizing a common property of different objects (like greenness of trees), and this is the beginning of science. But when the actual world is replaced in the mind by a symbolic world, it is much easier to think about it and to discover relationships which might remain hidden; like the truths of geometry.

This might seem to be an overwhelming case for the contention that human relations and ways of life are the result of the use of the human power of reasoning, i.e. the ability to arrive at rational consequences from the facts of experience, perhaps not all at once, but slowly and surely because, in the end, wrong interpretations are bound to be shown up as fallacious.

Yet at the end of the nineteenth century, the idea of the rationality of human life had to meet its greatest challenge, as the result of the work and ideas of Freud.

In a sense, the movement to which Freud belonged was a reaction against the nineteenth-century idea of man as a creature whose actions were determined mainly by reason. Freud found the real sources of human action to be often far from reasonable, and far different from what appeared on the surface.

The debate between 'reason' and 'passion' as the origin of human actions is, however, a very old one and opinions have wavered very considerably during the last three centuries. David Hume* argued that reason does not provide the driving force or impulse to action; it only decides the nature of the action, when the impulse, or what he called the 'passion', exists. It is very obvious that human beings are often subject to irrational impulses, which make them undertake actions which their reason, if it could operate impartially, would disapprove of. Sex, envy, anger, ambition, self-esteem, are powerful incentives to action, and often the individual cannot help himself. Hume saw reason in the very secondary role of planning actions which would enable a person to satisfy his uncontrolled impulses. 'Reason is and ought

---

* *Treatise on Human Nature*, 1739-1740.

to be only the slave of the passions', he declared, 'and can never pretend to any other office but to serve and obey them. . . .' Thus Hume thought that our 'passions' decide what we want to do and our reason helps us to plan ways of bringing it about.

Notwithstanding Hume, the eighteenth and nineteenth centuries liked to think of civilized men as eminently reasonable beings, whose actions were determined by a careful judgement of the circumstances, although it is not likely that everyone even in the 'age of reason' would go as far as the father of John Stuart Mill when he wrote, 'Every man possessed of reason is accustomed to weigh evidence and to be guided and determined by its preponderance when various conclusions are, with their evidence, presented with equal care and skill. There is a moral certainty, though some few will be misguided, that the greatest number will judge right and that the greatest force of evidence, whatever it is, will produce the greatest impression.'

By the end of the nineteenth century, the world was undoubtedly ripe for a reaction from this idea of man as pre-eminently a rational, thinking creature. It is likely that many people were seeking to escape from the straightjacket of Victorian rationality in which they found themselves. This movement found its leader in Sigmund Freud, who provided ample and convincing evidence of the irrationality of human beings and the importance, in determining conduct and attitudes, of impulses and urges having hidden and forgotten origins of which the subject might be totally unconscious.

Freud reached these conclusions from a study of mental abnormalities, which came to his notice first when, as a practising neuropathologist, he worked in the clinic of Jean Marcel Charcot in Paris and became acquainted with the hypnotic methods practised there. He also became interested in hysteria and, after some years' study of it, came to the conclusion that it had its origin in sexual maladjustments, which he attempted to cure, first by hypnosis, and later by asking the patient to talk freely until the cause of the trouble, which the patient had completely forgotten, was discovered. This was the method of 'free association', used by Freud, and developed by him into the basic method of psychoanalysis.

In order to explain his observations, Freud came to the conclusion that mental processes originate in an unconscious part of the mind. The idea of an unconscious part of the mind was not new. The mere existence of memory implies an unconscious, since everything one knows and can remember cannot be present in the consciousness at once. The whole idea of consciousness, which concerns itself with a few things at a time, implies an 'unconscious', even if it is only a store house. But there was much even in ordinary experience to indicate that the unconscious is more than this. Ideas often come into the consciousness spontaneously and more or less fully formed. This is true not only of recollections, where an idea, which has perhaps been forgotten, is recalled; but it is true also of new ideas and new combinations, such as a solution of difficulties, which often appear suddenly in the mind, and one cannot account for this appearance except as the result of unconscious mental activity. It is well known that important discoveries and artistic creation have often appeared in the minds of the discoverers without any apparent conscious effort. It is of course also true of the many everyday ideas which 'come into our minds'.

It would appear from this that the unconscious mind is not a purely passive receptacle, but a dynamic region in which symbols and images dissociate and recombine and appear in new combinations. Nevertheless the idea that the unconscious could be an active participant in the mind was resisted by the introspective psychologists of the nineteenth century. For example, William James listed in his *Principles of Psychology* ten proofs which had been given of unconscious mental activity, and dismissed them all.

For Freud, the unconscious was an active part of the mind of supreme importance. He regarded the mind as made up of three parts: the *id* which contains initially our instinctive equipment, i.e. everything present at birth; the *ego* (approximating roughly to the conscious mind), that part of the mind which is contributed by the individual and receives and interprets sensations from the outside world and contrives appropriate actions; and the *superego*, the part which represents the influence of parents, teachers, public opinion, and the influence of society.

Satisfactory actions, according to Freud, are ones which satisfy at the same time the demands of the id and of the superego. Hence arises the possibility of conflict if the individual is unable to find actions which satisfy their different requirements. An unresolved conflict leads to neurosis and other mental troubles. Desires arising in the id, but which are rejected by the superego, are repressed and become unconscious, but they may find an outlet in acts in which the person unconsciously betrays his secret wishes, his desire to do something which the superego regards as scandalous or even 'unthinkable'. Repressed wishes turned up in dreams which therefore offered the most direct way of learning the contents of the unconscious.

Freud's theory is a real scientific theory in that it attempts to make a model which enables us to understand the actions of human beings and even to predict them, and also to influence them. It based its claims on the success of its predictions and on its power to influence the behaviour of human beings. It was undoubtedly crude, but it was based on a direct appeal to experience. Freud stressed this: 'There is no other source of knowledge but the intellectual manipulation of carefully verified observation . . . and no knowledge can be obtained from revelation, intuition and inspiration.'*

His ideas about the mind were, however, completely disconnected with other parts of the developing scientific picture, and still are. They had no connection with neurophysiology (the study of the working of the brain), and if we accept the possible identification of the *id* with the older parts of the brain, no basis in brain mechanism is known.

But Freud's ideas had the other marks of successful scientific theories—the ability to illuminate other regions of experience and to energize innumerable researches.

Psychoanalysis became at once much more than a therapeutic method. In the hands of Freud it was used as a method of explaining the nature and development of mental attitudes. His idea of the id was that it was not just a repository of static instincts, but a dynamic growing thing which would undergo decisive and

---

* This appears to mean that intuition cannot take the place of observation. Freud's interpretations, especially in anthropology, are undoubtedly intuitional.

permanent modification during the life and development of the individual.

Looking for the sources of mental development, he found the decisive formative influences in very early life. Children, he said, pass through a phase of infantile sexuality, culminating in the fifth year. After this time it gradually recedes into the unconscious, returning in later life to determine adult attitudes. According to Freud, the genesis of neurosis in later life is usually to be found in early childhood.

The character-forming influences of childhood are thus derived from the triangle; self, father, and mother. As an integrated, wilful person, a child derives his aggressiveness and the desire to dominate, and to get what he wants. From the father—the stern, disapproving father of the Freudian mythos—he derives his feeling of right and wrong, his consciousness of guilt. From the mother he obtains love, security, and shelter. His feelings to his father are an ambivalent mixture of admiration and hatred; his love of his mother makes him jealous and possessive.

Out of this conflict of feelings the child develops its personality and may win through into an independent mentality, but the conflict leaves traces and may produce adult neurosis. For example, a man with excessive mother fixation would spend his life seeking for a woman on whom he can be dependent; or a woman will always be looking for someone with the authority of a father.

The most striking feature of Freud's work is the single-minded ruthlessness with which he probed into phenomena of every kind, attempting to find the remote causes of disconnected events. He had a great desire to classify and find principles of the greatest simplicity in complex events. For example, he attempted to reduce the human instincts to two basic instincts, one of which he called *eros* and the other the destructive instinct. *Eros* included the instincts of self-preservation and the preservation of the species (love of children and family) as well as sexual love. The destructive instinct, which gives rise to aggression and destructiveness, leads eventually to the end of all living things—death. The ultimate goal of all living organisms, he says, is death. 'Hence arises the paradoxical situation that the living organism struggles more energetically against events (dangers, in fact) which might help it to obtain its life's goal rapidly.'

He looks for the origins and meaning of social customs in human nature as he sees it today, and also to a considerable extent in his own outlook. It has been said that Freud saw the history of mankind as a reflection of the development of the individual man.

Freud went on to explore social aspects of human life from simliar points of view. Many of his ideas are quite frankly speculations. Human society began, he thought, as a primeval horde, a band of brothers, living under the subjection of a tyrannous and brutal father who owned all the females. When they found this intolerable, the sons had to go out into the wilderness and try to set up a new horde by the capture of females. But at last the brothers learnt to unite against the father and slew him and ate him, in order to acquire his strength and 'virtue.' This was the beginning of the community, for it taught them that they could achieve together what they could not do singly. The cannibalistic eating of the hated tyrant gave place, first to the eating of a substitute, in the form of a totem animal. The feelings of guilt which they subsequently felt led to the development of taboos, the renunciation of the totem animals, and the renunciation of the father's women, i.e. the mothers, and to attempts at expiation of the crime. Later the totem animal became a human god, to whom sacrifices were made by way of expiation of the original crime, leading up to the supreme sacrifice of an innocent man, the Son of God.

This is a very brief summary of Freud's remarkable theory of human social development, but it serves to illustrate the theoretical nature and intuitiveness of Freud's approach. He saw the restrictions imposed by a society in the same light as the restrictions imposed by a father on the child, and the idea of the tyrannical father and the rebellious son recurs again and again. His picture of the individual man was certainly greatly influenced by what he found in himself. This origin gives his work in some respects a rather dogmatic tone which is not present in other branches of science, although one must qualify this by saying that Freud often emphasized the speculative nature of his ideas.

The impact of Freud on the twentieth-century mind has been enormous. This was really because it exactly met the need of the moment—which was to escape from the excessive rationality of the Victorian epoch. It provided an excuse for escaping from the conventions of society, and as such was eagerly accepted by many people who wanted to discredit the idea of human relations they had had forced upon them. Tired of the conventions of a stiff and elaborate civilization, many people thought longingly of a life in which natural desires were not too closely cabined and confined, and they accepted with alacrity the contention that man was at the bottom irrational and that freedom from neurosis and mental conflict was to be found in accepting and acting on, instinctive urges without repression, and that this was also the secret of creative activity in literature and art.

But Freud himself, although he found the origins of mental illness in conflict and repression, had no doubt about their necessity as a condition of human society, and as a provider of the stimulus of individual achievement. While he believed that instinctive impulses were the driving force of human endeavour, he had no doubt that they had to be transformed or sublimated. 'Sublimation of instinct', he said, 'is an especially conspicuous feature of cultural evolution; this it is that makes it possible for the higher mental operations—scientific, artistic, ideological activities —to play such an important part in civilized life.'* So we come back to the constructive life of human beings in which they devote themselves as far as possible to the difficult task of living together, to trying to understand their surroundings, and to making use of their knowledge.

Freud's ideas are not really in contradiction with the obvious fact that human ways of living together are still based on knowledge and understanding. He deals with the basic impulses, still powerful in man, which are of deep significance in the life of every individual. His first concern is with the development of human attitudes from early years. But human life is not only a question of individual impulse, or even the interplay of impulses. Its main feature, which distinguishes it from other kinds of living,

---

* *Civilization and its Discontents*, p. 63.

is the existence of a superstructure of ideas and knowledge—a world of symbols and generalizations—which determines all activities. It cannot be said that Freud was unaware of the social nature of human life, but he does stress the conflict between the impulses of the individual and the requirements of society. As a practising physician he was first and foremost concerned with the human beings who were unsuccessful in resolving this conflict.

Freud dealt primarily with the individual, and does not stress the social nature of knowledge. What he called the super-ego is the shared knowledge of the community, which obviously does not belong to any one person but is necessarily a joint possession, mainly a gift from the past, something which precedes and survives all individuals. It is the atmosphere in which human life takes place and it is obvious that the 'rational' features of human life belong to it, since no formulation of experience is acceptable unless it is sufficiently rational. The private hallucinations and dreams of the individual do not belong to it unless they are sufficiently rational to be accepted.

The conflict between 'passion' and 'reason' is resolved if we remember that 'passion' arises from individual impulse, while 'reason' is the examination of the impulse which is made jointly by society.

Freud saw the super-ego mainly as a censor, which functions by restricting the actions of individuals into something which was in conformity with the common edifice of knowledge. It undoubtedly has this function but what Freudians do not stress is that it also has a creative function in providing the only medium by which the individual can realize his human potentialities. Alone he could do nothing. Without the framework of knowledge and symbolism a man is born into, he would be nothing but a moron.

The 'super-ego' may restrict the primitive impulses of individuals, but it is also the sole condition of the enjoyment of a fully human life. Conflict may certainly occur between the individual impulse and social necessity, but it is a necessary part of the human situation. It is not enough to deplore it as a misfortune, as the Freudians often seem to do, but we must also count it as a necessary feature of human life, because if the possibility of conflict did not exist, neither would the remarkable opportunities which the interaction of individual and society offers of enabling human ability and enjoyment to blossom and fructify.

The main problem of human life is how to create a super-structure of ideas and institutions which enable people to live together in a human way. I have suggested that to do this they must hold shared beliefs which provide values and meaning to human life.

No doubt these values are a reflection of human nature as it exists, but they are more than a reflection of primitive human nature because they aim at creating an 'unnatural' type of man—they aim at moulding human tendencies and impulses in a particular direction. All human life is unnatural, in that it is a creation of human ideas, and civilized life is especially so. The human species has become, as Paul Valéry said, 'remote from all the prime and normal conditions of life'. This sometimes causes neurosis and other ills, which might be avoided by a less unnatural way of living; but many people would like to have both the advantages of a highly developed civilization and all that implies, and at the same time personal 'freedom' to ignore whatever is inconvenient for themselves.

Chapter Sixteen

IMAGINATION IN HUMAN LIFE

IT MIGHT SEEM to be unnecessary in a book on the scientific views of life to discuss the imaginative activities of human beings. But as the human attitude to experience is essentially imaginative—by this I mean that in interpreting their sense impressions human beings go far beyond the simple direct and practical interpretations which an animal like a cat is obviously capable of—it is misleading not to mention the artistic products in which this is exhibited most directly.

Imagination is made possible by the human ability to find meanings which are expressed by symbols. It is by the manipulation of such symbols that the creative imagination largely operates. As I have pointed out, even language is essentially imaginative, since there is in most cases no logical or necessary connection between a word and what it represents. The use of such symbols also helps the interpretation of experience, because they provide a ready-made set of patterns into which experience can be fitted.

Even in making simple decisions we use the imagination because many imaginative possibilities present themselves, and we examine them and try to select the most rewarding. In the more subtle and abstruse issues, the meanings which we try to find in our experiences can only be expressed in imaginative terms.

It would not be too much to say that the whole creative output of human communities is imaginative, because before anything can be created it must be thought of or imagined. It is certainly true of scientific discovery that it involves the exercise of the imagination, because the new theory or law which connects and explains the various facts is necessarily an imaginative leap into the unknown.

If we think about our experiences in another way, we can see that our stream of consciousness is produced by the interaction of immediate experience with recollections of the past, which are used to help to interpret the present. These recollections have usually lost much unnecessary detail; only the significant and essential elements remain. What we are aware of is thus an amalgam of past and present in which sometimes the one and sometimes the other predominates. The past experience can be recalled by association and by symbols which may not correspond very closely with the experience they represent. Much of our time may be spent in this recollection of past experiences, and images derived from experience can easily be adduced by the use of symbols, so that the experiences and their symbolic expression are almost inextricably mixed.

Thus it comes about that human beings now, as always, spend much time in an imaginative world, with images stimulated by symbols, which may not correspond to any actual experience, but only to an imaginative construction.

The art of the story-teller—possibly the oldest of human arts—is to establish an imaginative reconstruction of events in the hearer by words. It is remarkable that words should have this power of stimulating imaginative images so that the whole situation becomes as real to the reader or listener as if he were an actual participant.

In one form or another this story-telling is a universal human practice. The result is that human beings are not content to live their own lives. They want to experience other lives as well—possibly more stirring and eventful than their own. They certainly get pleasure from living other lives imaginatively. This gives their own experience a multiplicity which adds enormously to the richness and content of life.

This is especially true at the present time when so many people live rather monotonous and dreary working lives. Outside working hours they seek 'entertainment', which often means taking part in story-telling in one of its many forms—reading, films, radio, television, or theatre. Besides conveying information about other ways of life, these all have the function of enlarging the individual life by offering substitutes or alternative situations. Life is then lived not in one dimension, but in a complex many-dimensional pattern of the actual and imagined.

The exercise of the imagination is obviously greatly helped by the resources of language which provide many words to represent acts and objects. Since they can be arranged in innumerable combinations, they offer an easy means for the creation of imaginative worlds.

Even at the dawn of recorded history, story-telling reached, in the *Odyssey* and *Iliad*, a level of artistry which has never been surpassed. In them are to be found every artifice and trick to hold attention and create interest: suspense, the slow building up of details to a climax, the contrasting anticlimax, allegory, a complete insight into human character, the appeal to human feelings of pity and generosity, the wider issues of human life, which come from the interplay of character, ambition and chance, and finally the uncertainties of life and the hardness of fate.

Nearly all these characteristics come into the short passage from the *Iliad* which I quote below: it is a sufficient example of all imaginative literature.

It is Andromache's lament for her husband:

'Alas, Hector, alas for me!' she cried, 'so you and I were born under the same unhappy star, you here in Priam's house and I in Thebe—you are on your way to Hades and the unknown world below; leaving me behind in misery, a widow in your house. And your son is no more than a baby, the son we got between us, we unhappy parents. You, Hector, now that you are dead, will be no joy to him, nor he to you. Even if he escapes the horrors of the Achean war, nothing lies ahead of him but hardships and trouble with strangers eating into his estate. . . . And you by the beaked ships, far from your parents, will be eaten by the wriggling worms when the dogs have had their fill, lying naked for all the delicate and lovely clothing made by women's hands that you possess at home. All of which I am going to burn to ashes. It is of no use to you, you will never lie in it. But the men and women of Troy shall accord you that last mark of honour.'*

Faced with eloquence like this it is perhaps not surprising that Plato, who was trying to find a rational basis of human society, should turn against poets and orators. He said he would have no

---

* *The Iliad*, translated by E. V. Rieu (Penguin).

poets in his Republic, because the poets were deceivers, since they produced imitations of reality which made it impossible to distinguish truth from untruth. They caused men to be enslaved by false ideas. 'We shall beg Homer and the other poets', he said, 'not to take it amiss if we raze these things, and such as these, not that they are not poetical, and pleasant to many to be heard; but the more poetical they are, the less ought they to be heard by children, and men who ought to be free. . . .'

However, Plato's advice which would deny to human beings their most human ability, has never been taken, and they continue to live in a phantasy world created by storytellers, as well as in the real one. As the real world becomes less urgent, the phantasy world becomes more necessary and important.

By what extraordinary mental alchemy is it that words produce this remarkable transference of ideas and feelings? It must surely have been one of the great early discoveries of the human race that language had such capabilities. I have already suggested that words have this power because of their generality; they are not the precise equivalent of what they represent, but they call up in the hearer or reader similar images drawn from his own experience, and they can do this because these images are themselves rather generalized and are in this respect not unlike the words.

Because language is a communication on this rather generalized plane, pictorial illustrations are usually unnecessary and in fact a hindrance in an imaginative work. The reader prefers to make his own construction of the story—he does not want someone else's. Illustrations also contain so much that is really irrelevent. When you read a story you do not want a photograph of the house in which the action takes place; you can quite easily imagine all the essentials, the rest is unimportant and is better left in the shadowy background. This is the reason why moving pictures so often seem curiously external—there is always so much irrelevant detail and there is nothing left for the imagination to work on: the audience is not allowed to make its own mental picture, i.e. to reconstruct the scene from its own experiences.

Turning now to other imaginative activities we also find that graphic arts of one kind or another have been universal features of human life. The earliest known works of man, the cave paintings of southern France and Spain, give us a vivid glimpse of the mind and work of those early men, the paleolithic hunters who ranged through Europe in the age of the bison and mammoth, long before the establishment of any urban or civilized life. This art is not only competent technically but clearly purposeful and apparently has a magical purpose—to give power and influence events on which human life is dependent.

It would appear that all primitive art is purposeful rather than representational; thus the object of statuary is not to copy objects as they exist (although in Egyptian tombs objects are placed which seem to be just models of everyday objects, they are also the symbols of things required by the deceased) but to create objects which have a significant meaning. Thus the statues of the rulers are not really lifelike, but are a realization of the idea of the monarch in his capacity as a warrior, or as a god. Similarly the masks and fetish objects which have been found among native tribes of Africa, up to the present day (like the judges' robes and wig in our own society) have as their object to increase the significance of the individual. They do this not so much by representing human characteristics, as by exaggerating them, so as to create feelings of awe and often of fear.

These few examples will suffice to show that the object of artistic creation in primitive society is neither representation i.e. to reproduce objects or happenings, nor to produce 'beautiful' objects. It is to create objects which have a significance of their own, and which are capable of influencing human feelings. The objects are therefore not copied from nature, but are imaginative variations, which emphasize some features at the expense of others.

It is the custom nowadays to regard painting as only recently delivered from the necessity of being representational and pictorial. It is true that until a hundred years or so ago most paintings told a story of one kind or another, but if you examine the older tradition of painting you will find it far from being photographic in its methods.

A glance at present-day illustrated papers shows how incapable a photograph is of conveying feeling. No one (except by accident) has ever produced a humorous photograph. When the newspapers want to convey humour or satire they have recourse to drawings in which the artist selects and exaggerates. The cartoon strip, which tells a story or creates a humorous situation, is completely impossible with a photographic technique. Even the advertisers usually make use of the artistic mode of representation rather than the photographic one. A glance at our papers shows that the use of drawings to induce feelings is as widespread now as ever.

During the long tradition of European painting the object has hardly ever been merely to convey information about persons, incidents, or scenes. Paintings are intended to convey the human meaning of the scene, or to induce feeling. Even the pictures representing particular incidents are utterly unlike a photographic representation of the scene, and this is not due to a lack of skill of the artists. Readers may have seen photographs, such as have occasionally appeared in the magazine *Life*, taken during some real happening like a murder. They will perhaps agree with me that such pictures convey little information and produce no emotion except a feeling of nausea and disgust. They merely show the externals of a squalid episode and reveal nothing of the feelings and motives of the participants.

The difference between a work of art and a photograph is that the former is organized to convey the maximum amount of meaning. Look at Pollaiaoulo's *Martyrdom of St. Sebastian*, for example, in the National Gallery, London. It sets the Christian resignation and unworldliness of the saint against the indifference and worldliness of the executioners. The figure and its background are set in the most vivid contrast; earthly scenes of the most beguiling kind are contrasted with the journey of the immortal soul to heaven, which is vaguely suggested by a light halo round the head of the martyr. It is obvious that this is a work both of artifice and of imagination. But it is not really an exceptional painting.

In all periods artists have not hesitated to depart from the strictly representational in order to convey feeling and meaning. They have used every kind of means at their disposal and within their imaginative resources to make and underline the effect they want to create. They not only use symbolism of obvious and subtle kinds; they practise every kind of distortion when it suits them.

K

The nature of the symbolism has naturally varied from one age to another in accordance with the main currents of feeling. In Byzantine art an impression of spirituality predominates. Men and women scarcely exist as human beings. but only as spiritualized embodiments who have lost many of their earthly attributes.

The motive of mediaeval Christian art was of course religious, but it never became solely a medium of conveying information, of being the illiterate man's bible. The object of the pictures and sculptures is always to convey the religious feeling; and the innumerable martyrdoms, crucifixions, last judgements, and holy families are commentaries on the Christian attitude to life, and aim not merely to convey the mere facts, but to convey the whole feeling of the Christian attitude. They used every possible device of emphasis and distortion to heighten the effect. No one could call these works representations of actuality; they are imaginative interpretations. Even the incidentals of the scene were objects chosen as symbols having definite associations.

The secular backgrounds which appeared in pictures later than the fourteenth century seem to me to be not so much representations of actual scenes as a kind of idyllic utopia; a reminder of the loveliness which the earth might possess or which might be created. It is here, peeping out of the background of religious pictures, with their emphasis on sacrifice and eternity, that we see visions of an earthly paradise—perhaps the beginning of the secular outlook and interest in the world which led to the development of science.

When, at the time of the Renaissance, knowledge of the achievements of antiquity burst upon the European world, it brought into painting a new objective—the conscious attempt at creating beauty of form. The Greeks had sought perfection. They admired the human body, but as most human beings failed to come up to the highest conception of beauty they attempted to create the perfection of form in their statues. This search for the perfect or ideal representation permeated their sculpture, as it did much of their philosophical thought. The Italian School of the Renaissance took over the Greek idea of the naked human form as a subject of art, and side by side with religious paintings they took subjects from the pagan myths of the ancient world, which permitted them to indulge the sensual pleasure of the eye and in doing so they sought to re-create the vanished idyllic springtime of the human race, and to reconstruct a world which was the direct opposite of the Christian outlook, not only in its frank acceptance of the world as it is, but also in its acceptance of sensuous and amoral day-dreaming of a world which never had and never could exist. So frankly fantastic symphonic compositions were produced, such as the enormous allegorical paintings of Tintoretto and Titian—in which human bodies became parts of vast schemes of decoration, and no one thought it odd to see them floating through the air, with an attendant swarm of chubby cherubs.

Like most human activities, something begun for one purpose was found to be satisfying for another. For one thing, painters liked painting, and they painted for the pleasure of it. Paintings began to be enjoyed as 'works of art', both on account of the skill of the painter and in admiration of what he had done with paint, and because of their imaginative content, as opening windows to other worlds. Painting thus became an independent art, a medium for the exercise of the imagination which could both give an imaginative reconstruction of the actual world and could also on occasion bring to life epochs and episodes remote in space and time. Paintings were commissioned and bought as decorations not merely because they were beautiful as decorations, but also as backgrounds for (and to give perspective to) the life of the time. At a time when the life of cities was both colourful and infused with symbolism, paintings could both increase the colour and extend the range of the symbolism.

Other paintings illustrated the life of the times; character portraits of the great and also of the insignificant; pictures of domestic life, as well as of public occasions. All these themes were treated imaginatively and with insight. Painting was like the novel of today in being a commentary on life. European civilization is unique in possessing this imaginative and pictorial record of its life for several centuries. The fact that such a record exists is an illustration of the peculiarly imaginative nature of the mind of western man and of its ingrained habit of seeking for symbols of reality, and combining them in always-new creations.

The artist must not only create harmony, he must also create a perspective—the perspective of imagery in which every part serves the whole conception and the whole arises naturally from the parts. It is this preoccupation with structure and composition which has made painters indifferent to the subject matter of their paintings and indeed predisposed to subjects having no intense human feeling; for example, still-life subjects, in which they could concentrate on the problems of abstraction, form, and structure.

In the second half of the nineteenth century, concern with such problems became the predominant issue for many painters. It might be thought that the discovery of photography released them from the necessity of illustrating and commenting on contemporary life. I do not think this is true because, whatever its temporary aberrations, the main tradition of painting was always imaginative. Yet painters did begin to concern themselves increasingly with the external world of light and colour and with creating structural harmonies having no human implications at all. They were concerned with the harmonies to be found in the world of nature, filled as it is with shapes and forms in endless combination. In some ways these paintings are less imaginative and much more a rendering of nature than the earlier story-pictures. Human relations—even the world considered as a habitat for man—are ignored. Such a simple sensual pleasure in nature is akin in some ways to the feeling of Chinese art in its concentration on nature, but it showed a more eager exploration of new ideas.

The painters' vision of the man-less world was often very different to that of the ordinary man. Painters like Cezanne and Van Gogh stressed unfamiliar aspects of the outside world such as the primal energy and exuberance of life and its underlying structure. Their pictures are both imaginative creations and exact representations of an aspect of the world. They are imaginative because they extract aspects of the familiar world which are not evident to the ordinary man and weave them into a new synthesis. They are in a sense scientific because they are true to nature.

We should not ask for verisimilitude in a work of art. Like the musician, the artist creates his own language, and the only criterion is that it must be able to express aspects of experience which are communicable. We do not ask him to dot all his i's and cross all his t's. He appeals direct to our essential vision, taking what he thinks significant and leaving the rest. It does not worry us if a cartoonist draws people with heads as big as their bodies, or if the comic artist suggests the expression on the face with a dot and a line or two. That is how we can see them and it is enough. Matisse can suggest a human figure and make it a thing of beauty and significance with a single thin line. In doing this he is appealing to the universal human faculty of abstraction. His drawings are discoveries in the nature of experience.

We might ask, if painting is an exercise of the imaginative and creative faculties, is it necessary to have any recognizable features at all, any resemblances to the world? Why not purely abstract exercises in form and colour? This is in fact what some recent movements in art have attempted. In following Cezanne, cubism attempted a more thorough exploration of structure, endeavouring to reduce nature to an almost geometrical conception of lines and surfaces. It is more difficult to produce convincing works of art by this method, since the greater the degree of abstraction the harder it is to appeal to or create similar images in the viewer's mind; and the abstract painter if he fails in his main symbolic scheme is unable to fall back on the verisimilitude of his symbols —the fact that they do mean *something* to the uninitiated—even if they do not convey the desired effect. Many valid works of art have undoubtedly been created in this technique—for example, the paintings of Braque; and no one can deny that significant forms of experience have been discovered, which in their turn have influenced the modern vision, as can be seen from popular art everywhere.

Picasso and others have attempted synoptic vision, i.e. to combine multiple impressions of an object in a single picture, e.g. to show a face at the same time in profile and in full front view Picasso's motives however are profoundly human and some of his pictures as e.g. Guernica, are filled with a particular symbolism with which he makes a direct and bitter comment on human beings and human affairs. Life is no longer seen as an idyll. It is a bitter conflict between good and evil; and the good is weak and despairing and the evil immensely strong and almost triumphant.

In the early years of this century psychoanalysis and the study of unconscious motivation also had a profound influence. If art is imagination, why not make use of the crude images rising from the subconscious? Here according to Freud were the real roots of life and conduct. Why not take the symbols as they come, without attempting to rationalize them and fit them into a naturalistic order? The making of a picture was itself a kind of analysis; the symbols which it produced naturally belonged to the dream world. In the works of Chagall animal heads appeared on human bodies and human anatomy suffered the strangest transformations. Man the planner, the thinker, and the creator disappeared, so did the common aspects of human life; and we were left with a world in which the distinction between the human and the animal, between the animate and inanimate, is not very apparent. All that remained was a kind of pregnant form, a world of embryonic shapes and patterns, waiting to be endowed with specific properties.

Others like Chirico and Salvador Dali produced visions of other worlds—for example, lonely human beings existing in an endless desert, marked only by the few ruins of an ancient civilization (the present one?). In these pictures the mind is taken to a point from which the present world can be seen as from a remote distance. The human horizon is enlarged by the glimpse of another 'possible world'. But it would seem that in these and many similar pictures the heightening of the imaginative content of the picture has been achieved at the expense of a loss of its abstract qualities. The imaginative content of these pictures is in fact rammed home by the use of a photographic degree of realism.

In the brief space I have left I cannot do much more than mention the development of music, but it is necessary to mention it because it is the best and clearest example of the human habit of abstracting relations and patterns from the sensual data and finding pleasure in them as they are and in all the combinations which can be made from them.

Why do some musical sounds or combinations of musical sounds give pleasure and have significance? This is one of the most difficult aesthetic problems, and since nearly everyone finds pleasure in music at one level or another, its solution will be bound to tell us much about human ways of using experience. It might be thought that the significance in music is derived from association. Certain kinds of music are traditionally associated with certain feelings. This is probably so, for music undoubtedly began with song and dance as a language or perhaps an *enlargement* of language to add emphasis and feeling. Dr Colles finds the origin of all music in 'human impulses finding expression through the voice'. Commenting on this, Frank Howes says, 'Others may think the rhythmic impulse with its roots in the ordinary physical activity of the body to be the primary source of music. But whether dance or song came first, rhythm or melody, their main constituents are both necessary to music, which thus has its origin in anything but pure instrumental composition.'*

But language itself was probably once far more expressive than it is now, and used intonation as well as articulation. Just as poetry came before prose, perhaps singing came before talking. But it may have been too expressive, so for ordinary purposes language shed the emotional overtones and became a comparatively placid and unexciting medium of communication. The music was kept for special occasions when it was desired to heighten the significance. Musical instruments, such as drums, horns, and pipes, were also used for this purpose, and as a background for voices. Ancient authors often refer to the great emotional power of music. 'Music enters into the inner recesses of the soul', says Plato, 'and lays powerful hands upon it.' It is recorded that Pythagoras, seeing a young man so inflamed with jealousy, music, and evil as to be resolved to set fire to his mistress's dwelling, restored the lover to reason by causing the flute player to change from the Phrygean mode to a soft soothing air!† Men have gone to battle until quite recently to the sound of drums and trumpets. This was supposed to encourage them and make them oblivious and careless of danger.

---

* Frank Howes, *Man, Mind and Music*, Secker & Warburg, London.

† A similar effect is being produced in certain classes at the present time by a kind of music called Rock and Roll, which apparently excites young people to riot and act violently and without inhibitions. No one seems to have tried soothing them by a change of mode! However no modern music seems to equal in potency the baleful music of Duke P'ing of Chin, when 'drawn by the magic of an evil tune, eight huge black birds swooped down from the south and danced on his terrace, black clouds blotted out the sky, a tempest tore down the hangings of his palace, broke the ritual vessels, hurled down the tiles from the roof, the King fell sick and for three years no blade of grass grew in Chin and no tree bore fruit'. (Arthur Waley, *The Analects of Confucius*).

Musical sounds are also made to heighten the significance of ceremonial occasions, and to accompany ritual and drama. Its purpose is to underline the meaning and to increase the emotional impact.

From being an accompaniment of action designed to emphasize and add emotion and feeling, music has largely become a substitute of action—a kind of shadow action which takes place in the mind. Instead of the actual march of the soldiers you have the military march; instead of the actual dance, the dance of rhythms in the mind. It is obvious that music as a language is so much more general than words—it does not call up specific incidents; it can refer to any incidents, or to none.

Music thus becomes a very abstract expression of human experience and feeling, usually divorced from specific occasions, and having its own structure and rules.

Another element in music is the ability of human beings to take pleasure in patterns and textures of sound, in the progression and development of complex sequences of phrases which follow their own internal necessity. The ability to take intense pleasure in such sequences is a consequence of human preoccupation with abstract forms, and performing and listening to music has an element of play in it—the pleasure of exercising an ability for the fun of it.

But it is quite probable that purely abstract pattern and shape is not enough, and that some emotional association is present in nearly all musical compositions. If we do not know the association the music is apt to be meaningless. We can make very little of music when we do not know the idiom; for example, easterners can make little sense of western music, and *vice versa*.

It is perhaps not more surprising that we are able to find meaning in patterns of sound than in the more specialized sound of words. If the brain can interpret the complicated patterns into which our ears translate the rather subtle sounds of words, may we not allow it the ability to find emotional as well as intellectual meanings in pure music?

They are usually meanings which are not exactly expressible in words. For one thing the meaning of music is much less definite than the meaning of words. Everyone can make his own interpretation, and the meanings found by different people will no doubt depend on their own emotional background. You often cannot say in words what a piece of music is about, yet it certainly moves you and you recognize it as a valid expression of experience, something which makes satisfying sense.

Sir Donald Tovey claimed that there is nothing in purely instrumental music which does not explain itself. We can take this to mean that it is an independent mode of expression, of a greater degree of abstraction than speech. It will combine with speech in every proportion; it is capable of any desired degree of association with concrete meanings, as we see when we consider the enormous variety of music from programme music to almost purely abstract compositions, and from popular songs to jazz and opera. That the human mind has been capable of creating an independent mode of conveying thought and feeling, and developing it to such an extent and with such a universal appeal, is one of the best examples of its faculty for abstraction and its habitual substitution of remote abstractions for acts and things.

The constant human preoccupation with imaginative constructions which express the meaning and significance to be discovered in one aspect or another of experience is sufficient to discredit the idea which has been advocated by the communist writers that the sources of human advance and creativeness are essentially economic—that useful discoveries are only made in the attempt to solve practical and urgent problems. It may well be that practical needs stimulate inventiveness; but the universal occurrence of artistic expression in every conceivable medium shows that human beings have normally lived in an imaginative world of their own making; and have used every medium available to them to heighten and embellish this imaginative world.

There have been times in human history when there was little room for imaginative activities—when necessity and poverty left no opportunity for cultivation of the decoration and embellishment of life. Certainly the industrial revolution reduced many human beings to the level when economics—earning the daily bread—was all that life offered. But this should not be taken as the normal mode of human living, or an indication of the basic motive of human life. The long history of human arts shows that life is completely human only in so far as opportunities for imaginative activities exist.

Chapter Seventeen

SCIENCE AND THE FUTURE OF HUMANITY

WE ARE already well advanced in the revolution of human life caused by scientific advances. By and large it has brought about a widespread improvement in the material conditions of life in many parts of the world. People consume more, and more varied, food, they do not work so hard, they live in better houses, and they travel about more. They are provided with all sorts of amenities which are the products of scientific discovery; new synthetic materials make it possible to fabricate all kinds of articles cheaply; homes have been brightened up with new paints, constant entertainment is available on the television, ready-cooked foods are waiting in the refrigerator; in hot climates it is no longer necessary to endure the heat; the telephone is at hand whenever one wishes to talk to a friend. People also live much longer and much of the insecurity of life, especially in large towns, has disappeared.

It might seem, then, that science has fulfilled the promise it offered in the early years of this century of making life altogether easier and brighter. At that time the only serious problem remaining appeared to be how to occupy people's leisure when all the work which had to be done took only two or three hours a day.

On the whole this promise of a world-wide Utopia has not been realized. The general increase in standards of living is found in practice to be limited by various factors, economic and political, which affect some countries more than others. In Britain the lack of raw materials makes it necessary for a very large part of the production to be exported to secure what are required, and this export is being conducted under increasingly unfavourable conditions. However in the U.S.A., an area with vast natural resources and rather thinly populated, conditions are much more favourable and the material standard of living has gone up to an unprecedented level, and may be taken as an indication of the kind of society an unhindered application of scientific techniques will produce.

But although many parts of the world have shared in a great improvement in living standards, it does not seem to produce contentment, or even stability. People who are well fed and well housed are not necessarily happy. Relatively high rates of pay do not prevent people wanting more and feeling angry and frustrated if they do not get it. A generally high standard of living does not prevent acute social conflicts. It is obvious that scientific and industrial civilization, even when it provides a high standard of living, does not necessarily produce a happy society.

This is due partly to the nature of the work, which is often tedious and repetitive. The workers feel they are just adjuncts of the machines and are unable to feel any personal interest in what they are turning out. But it is due much more to the lack of a satisfactory life outside the factory. Industry has in fact overlooked the fact that the worker is a human being and that he works on in order to live and not *vice versa*.

However, human beings can really put up with a good deal of monotony, which may even be healthful in giving them a chance for day-dreaming. They have been extraordinarily adaptable in the ways of making a living, and there is no real reason why they should not absorb the necessary boredom of a mass-producing age and make something human out of it.

What modern industrial societies such as our own (and these problems are probably more acute in Britain than in any other country) have failed to realize, are the minimum requirements of a happy contented human life. This is due to a separation of the roles of the human being as a worker and as an individual.

The objective of life is taken to be enjoyment, and this is universally regarded as a question of consumption. Newspapers, films, radio, all hold up as the reward of success a conspicuous expenditure on food, drink, parties, travel, and clothes. No one would deny that these are pleasurable and also reasonable incentives to effort, but when you have on the one hand a vast majority of workers who are unsatisfied in most of these amenities, and on the other the use of the means of mass communication to bring before them vividly, emotionally, and in great detail, the most lavish examples of this kind of consumption which can be found or imagined, the conflict between the wish and the achievement, between the drab reality and the dream, is inevitable. If the unobtainable carrot is continuously held in front of the donkey, it is not surprising that in the long run it will find a diet of hay unappetizing.

It is overlooked that high consumption is not the only condition of happiness, which has often been produced on the basis of very slender resources. Human beings often get intense satisfaction in performing tasks involving great hardship and difficulty. It may be said that it is only the exceptional man who subordinates everything to achieve an ambition; and who will regard the achievement as a sufficient reward; but the fact is that happy communities have existed on a much lower standard of living than is common now.

The main necessity is that the community must feel that its life is valuable, and this obviously implies a sense of values, which makes what has to be done seem to be worthwhile.

What is lacking in modern industrial society, but has been achieved at times in much less developed communities, is the integration of the individual with the community so that the society forms a sufficiently vivid background and provides strong incentives, arising from its own nature, to make necessary tasks seem valuable and worth while. To achieve this the society must have objectives which are not purely economic. As I have pointed out, this can only be provided by a social organization which emphasizes living rather than working as the objective; and this requires a clear sense of values.

At the present time relief from boredom is sought in the substitute life offered by entertainments like the cinema, television, radio, and organized sports. Up to a point this is undoubtedly good since, as we have seen, it is part of the human way of life to have one's own experience enlarged by imaginative participation in other kinds of lives. But it is not at all healthy when this kind of wish fulfilment occupies much of the thoughts of a large part of the population, and when there is such a contrast between the reality and the dream.

At times in human history there has been a flowering of human life, made possible by the existence of such a happy coincidence of individual effort and social possibility. At the present time there is a clear and obvious discrepancy between the possibility and the realization.

This discrepancy has been greatly accentuated in modern industrial civilization, by its sharp distinction between working and living, and one consequence of scientific discovery must be regarded as the break up of an integrated mode of life, which, as we have seen, is the normal and necessary mode of living of human beings. In the long run science is only capable of ameliorating the human lot provided that it is absorbed into an essentially human way of life, i.e. one which provides a reasonable outlet for the full abilities of well-integrated human beings.

Besides these general trends which have really been operative all this century, and much longer, there are at the present moment of human history some special problems, also brought about by scientific discovery. In the last twenty years, a radical change in the conditions of human life has been brought about by the discovery of how to make use of atomic energy. This energy is undoubtedly capable of continuing and extending the scientific revolution, by providing cheap power in parts of the world which have been lacking in natural power resources. The raw material used, uranium, is neither a very common element, nor a scarce one. It is a kind of residue from the enormous forces of creation, which produced the world and the stars. There is no doubt enough of it to solve to a great extent all human needs for power. There will be plenty of power for most purposes.

On the other hand this new source of power provides weapons of enormous and disastrous potency. Every new discovery of offensive weapons has led to great political consequences and it is too much to expect that the discovery of atomic weapons will not give rise to great changes in the political organization of human beings on the world. In human history, success and survival have nearly always gone to groups which, by luck or intelligence, possessed the better weapons. Over and again civilizations have been overcome by *force majeure*. Even the dominance of the white races over the rest of the world from 1500-1900 was based on superior weapons and other technological techniques. There is thus every reason to expect that the emergence of new and infinitely more powerful military weapons will lead to great political changes. It is obvious that in the long run the only possible method of control of such vast energies is a world-wide one, which can only mean a single all-powerful world authority. The only real question is its nature.

It has often been said that the very size of these forces is itself a guarantee that they cannot be used, since their use would obviously bring about complete disaster to both sides. This may well be the case, but the equilibrium of two equal and opposite forces is an unstable one. Equilibrium assumes perfect stability on both sides. In a tug of war the two opposing forces may be equal, but the victory goes to the one which lasts longest. We therefore cannot suppose that the state of balance between two forces will necessarily last indefinitely. One side or the other may in the long run disintegrate internally, and then the threat alone of overwhelming offensive power would be sufficient to secure domination.

It might be said that human ingenuity, which has in the past absorbed so many new situations, will again succeed in adapting itself to this one. It might be regarded as a good sign that even in the last three hundred years there has been a great diminution of the areas in which armed conflict is possible.

It might be thought that, now we are faced with such dreadful alternatives, there is every inducement for this process to continue.

It is difficult to feel very optimistic about this possibility. It is an unfortunate fact that human beings have rarely had much control over their political destiny. The amalgamation of two groups of people with divergent aims has very rarely been achieved by agreement, but nearly always by compulsory absorption of one group in the other.

The reason for this lies in human nature itself, in the way human beings cohere into a society. They are not, as I have already pointed out, well equipped for combined action. Individual men and women are beautiful and extremely efficient organisms for living their own lives. They can do what they want with considerable accuracy and in planning a course of action are able to take a very large number of factors, past and present, into account. Difficulties begin when they attempt combined action. This is implicit in the human situation because of the isolation of human individuals, who have no way of sharing experiences directly. The normal method of communicating with others, by means of speech, is a very indirect one. You cannot really communicate to another person exactly what you see and still less what you feel about it. You can only communicate in symbols which you hope will call up the response you expect. Owing to the ambiguity and inadequacy of words and the fact that the response depends on the listener's own experience, communication is rarely complete and often very imperfect. Of course people are often not clear in their own minds about what they want to communicate. The act of communicating compels clarification. What we say often depends on what we can find words to say clearly. But putting an idea into words often distorts the issue as well as clarifying it. For these reasons accurate communication is often difficult, and this makes it difficult for human beings to unite in action even in simple projects. The difficulty is greater the greater the number of persons involved.

In considering a course of action one person can grasp what is at stake and perhaps make a reasonable estimate of the consequences. A group of people will see things from different points of view. They will all see the situation in terms of their own mental picture—they will try to judge it in the light of their own experience, and their habitual attitudes and sometimes their personal interests will be involved. Of course, studying the situation from different points of view is an advantage in that it brings out considerations which might be overlooked, but it also leads to indecision and makes definite decisions and united action difficult.

In small communities it is possible for the people concerned to grasp the issues and arrive at a common course of action by discussion. Under these conditions public interest is not essentially different to self interest. The problems are problems of real men and women, of people you know or at least of people very like the people you know and understand.

The situation is very different in the urban communities of the present day, where the scale and complexity is too vast for anyone to grasp. Human beings may be able to make a reasonable judgement of matters arising within their own range of knowledge and experience, but the issues of international and even national politics are not simple and often cannot be grasped without special knowledge. They have to be communicated to the mass of people in a very simplified form and, as we know, it is only too easy for them to be carried away by a formula which has emotional overtones. In fact in democracies the people who have the knowledge and have to make decisions are often limited by having to keep within an accepted formula, which they know to be wrong. It is also only too easy for politicians to carry people with them by formulating a situation in highly simplified but tendentious terms. So we cannot have much hope that great wisdom will be exhibited in the future large-scale relations of mankind, and it can only be a great misfortune that human beings have at their disposal such enormous forces, which they are quite clearly not equipped to control, either by inborn ability or experience gained so far.

A final result of science, of which the consequences are yet to appear, is the enormous reduction in mortality from diseases and other accidents. This has already led, particularly in countries with an already large population and a low standard of living, to a steady increase in population, and it is quite obvious that whatever improvements are made in agriculture and food production, they are bound in time to overrun their food supply. The consequences of such a happening in nature are quite simple; overpopulation is followed either by expansion into greater territory or by famine, until the population falls to an equilibrium value.

It is difficult to see how the increasing populations of the east will be restrained from expanding into any part of the world which is capable of supporting them. It is almost certainly true that the food production of some parts of the world is capable of being greatly increased. One effect of medical science is to make the tropics a healthy environment for man, and now that nearly all infectious diseases have been conquered, a great increase of population in the tropical areas of South America and Africa is possible and likely. Much may also be done to make the deserts fruitful. All that is required is a supply of fresh water, and it is probably not beyond the resources of modern science and industry to find ways both of developing an economy which uses it in rather limited quantities, and of providing it in such quantities.

All this may lead to the movement of the centre of gravity of human life towards the tropics; but it is hard to see how in the future great population conflicts can be avoided. The continents are rather small regions; and now that there are no more frontier regions to be discovered, mankind, which has always been expanding from the settled into undeveloped regions, is faced with a final limitation. It will have to put up with the earth as it is.

Judging by the popularity of stories about space travel, many human beings are already feeling an urge to escape from the limitations of the earth. But here again we are faced with a real limitation imposed by nature—the colossal isolation of the earth. The difficulties of space travel are greatly under-estimated by enthusiasts. It is just conceivable that after years of effort and tremendous cost (which would be better spent on improving the earth) it will be possible to reach the other planets of the solar system, although it is unlikely that any will be found tolerable for human life. But so far as visiting and even having communication with possible inhabitants of worlds attached to other suns is concerned, even the nearest are utterly remote and beyond reach in any foreseeable future. The human being is isolated on his little earth for now and always. He has acquired a brain and intelligence which enable him to look into the depths of space, only to find that what he sees there is beyond his reach. So man has somehow to learn to be content with his little world. He will never know what is going on in Orion and what the life force has brought forth in distant corners of the universe. Perhaps the lesson in this is to be humble and try to make the most of life as we find it.

Chapter Eighteen

CONCLUSION

> No-one has ever explained what we men are, and that
> peculiarity of ours which is the mind. Mind is an inter-
> nal power which has involved us in an extraordinary
> adventure; our species has become very remote from
> all the prime and normal conditions of life. We have
> invented a world of our mind, and we want to live in that
> world of our mind.
> PAUL VALÉRY, *Reflections on the World To-day*

WE STARTED by asking the question: What is the nature of human
beings? Perhaps enough has been said to dispose of some of the
oversimple answers which have been given. There is no simple
answer. I hope I have at least given some idea of the great
complexity of human nature, and shown how little we know and
how unwise it is to be dogmatic notwithstanding all that has been
discovered and the very real progress of science. There has undoubtedly been a tendency among scientists to think they have
found the secret of life and mind in one aspect of it. Because they
contain mechanical contrivances, living things were regarded as
machines; because they were made of chemical substances, life
was a chemical phenomenon; because the nervous tissue conducts
electrical currents, the brain is likened to a telephone exchange.
These are all grotesque simplifications—but they satisfy the
human urge for at least a little understanding and comprehension.

Other scientists have always been aware of the great regions of
which very little knowledge exists. No one can predict what the
scientific picture of the world will be like in a hundred years, and
it may well be as different from the present day one as ours is from
that of a hundred years ago. Vast unsuspected regions may be
waiting for exploration, and the emphasis may be quite different.
The universe, if I may hazard a guess, may seem to be permeated
with life, and mind may appear not as a seemingly casual byproduct

but at different levels almost ubiquitous. Humanity has obviously only just begun to explore its own potentialities, and it can hardly be doubted that a time will come when the extraordinary abilities of human brains will be better understood and more widely used.

We have seen human beings as efficient, knowledgeable, intelligent, passionate, imaginative, and often creative beings. I have argued that all these qualities are all possessed in varying degrees by all, or nearly all human beings.

In the first place we saw them engaged in interpreting their sense impressions, and organizing them into coherent 'pictures'. This is life on the level of the higher animals. Beyond it come the much more complex modes of organizing experience which are peculiar to human beings. These methods arise from and utilize one basic human ability, the power of replacing directly apprehended experience by more abstract mental equivalents, i.e. by symbols, which can be used in their place. Everything human seems to spring from this power of dealing with experience at more than one stage of abstraction.

We have seen that this method of organizing experiences has given rise to:

1. The transmission and sharing of experience, through which human knowledge has become cumulative.

2. The analysis of experience, leading to a knowledge of how phenomena are related to each other and ultimately to science.

3. The creative transformation of symbols into new and imaginative combinations, from which inventions and artistic productions are derived.

4. The construction of human societies, based on a sharing of experiences by the use of symbolic equivalents and the creation of a symbolic framework to life which provides common and continuing objectives.

5. The replacement of appetite and instinct as the main sources of activities by motives and objectives based on the symbolic outlook.

Because of this, man lives a double life. He is at once an individual pursuing his own objectives according to his own judgement and according to the information he has; he is also a member of society in which everything he does is part of a larger pattern. It is not that he can be an individual or a part of a community at will. He cannot dissociate himself from human society and remain human. Practically all his ideas, his words, interpretations, objectives, come from the community.

While in a sense he makes his own picture of the world, the interpretation of the picture is a shared one, arrived at by gener-ations of his predecessors. A man therefore lives at one and the same time in the real directly apprehended world (what he sees and hears), and in a world of symbols (like words), which although it is in a sense a reflection or reconstruction of the real world, is also different because it is a world of meanings and significances. The meanings are an interpretation in symbols of what has been learnt from the past.

The symbolic world in which human beings live is more than the actual world; it includes, in a sense, something from all the actual worlds which have ever existed. Human beings therefore live in the past as well as in the present. The past continues and is here with us in the world of symbols with which we replace and interpret our actual world, and in the same way our own present will go on into the future.

It may be said that this view of human nature is based on the activities of exceptional people—the inventive and imaginative people who think for themselves, have new ideas, and possess the energy and drive to realize them, and it is not characteristic of the bulk of mankind who are and always have been unoriginal and rather unimaginative, and are content to live the life they have been brought up to and, in fact, are hostile to new ideas and always resistant to innovation.

There is of course some truth in this, but I have tried to show that creative ability in both science and art is the result of the use of ways of handling experience which are a common human possession; they are no more than a heightened form of human abilities which are possessed by everybody and used by everybody in the ordinary business of living, and without which a human life cannot be lived at all. We are obliged to be inventive in everyday life; we are frequently, in a sense, creative, since we think of new combinations and ways of solving our problems; we are all imaginative because we cannot help it. The creative genius uses these same abilities—perhaps more favourably developed by natural ability, education, opportunity, and compelling interest, and more effectively and with greater concentration on particular objectives. Even under relatively unfavourable conditions for its emergence, the sum total of human creativity has been very great, and many of its contributions have been from the relatively obscure. The human achievement has been continuous. It has gone on through all catastrophes and every kind of disaster. When the opportunity has occurred, human beings have invented, created, and built elaborate systems of thought, argued about their experiences, recalled the past, dreamed and imagined. It does not appear that the quality of human ability has increased since the beginning of historic times, although the amount varies with opportunity. The potteries and bronzes produced in the early periods of Chinese civilization, 5,000 years ago, are not exceeded by the artistic products of any other age; Greece at the dawn of history produced the *Iliad* and *Odyssey*; in the golden age of Greece a standard of intellectual lucidity was reached which has never been surpassed. One is entitled to argue from these visible peaks of achievement that the possible level of human ability has always been high. One gets the impression of vast reserves of potential ability waiting for a chance to develop.

We know little or nothing of the circumstances which led or permitted the development of the human brain, which enables us to perform acts of great skill for which no parallel can be found in nature or in primitive life. Who would have guessed a few hundred years ago that the whole population could learn to read and would read for pleasure; that reading newspapers would be a *relaxation*. Yet there seems no reason to doubt that the ability made use of has been present in human beings for many thousands of years—perhaps not entirely unused, but certainly not fully used. One wonders what unsuspected abilities may not be found in the future; if people may not perform with ease mental operations which seem to us very difficult.

A great deal of latent ability obviously comes to nothing owing to lack of opportunities—the possessor not being present in the right place and at a suitable time. For example in the late eighteenth century only small numbers of people could have had the opportunity of being educated as musicians, yet how many superlatively good musicians and composers were found in fairly small communities. It must be supposed that a great many potential musicians did not get this chance. How many labourers, bakers, and soldiers would have turned into Beethovens if they had a chance? Creation and invention seem to depend mainly on opportunity; the human ability is always there ready to develop when circumstances are favourable.

I am not arguing that all human beings are geniuses, but they do possess the same kind of faculties. They need to live a life which offers scope for imagination as well as for a reasonable amount of satisfaction of appetites. They need, in fact, the opportunity to live an essentially human life—that is to make use of all their human faculties, mental and physical.

It is obvious that human brains often do not get enough occupation in modern life, and they seek avidly for more, hence cross-word puzzles and other mental games. The trouble with the modern world is not that there is not enough intelligence for its needs, but that it does not know how to use the vast resources of brain power and intelligence which exist: in other words it does not know how to make use of the full abilities of human beings. It is a real deprivation for human beings to be unable to make full use of their extraordinary power of action, judgement and appreciation.

It is sufficiently obvious that no conclusive answers have been found to the questions which were asked at the beginning. It cannot be claimed at present that science can offer solutions to many of the problems of human life. Science has undoubtedly brought about great changes in the human outlook and has greatly increased the power of human beings and their ability to control their environment and themselves. It has demonstrated the unity of all life, and has revealed it as an age-long process, proceeding under the action of natural laws, which are at least partly understood. But life, even as we see it, transcends the limited horizons and the understanding of individual men and perhaps of the whole earth-bound race. Science has revealed a universe of colossal dimensions, emerging from an unknown past and proceeding towards an unpredictable future. That this visible universe is rich in life is hardly to be doubted, although we have and can hardly expect to obtain any certain knowledge of most of it, since it is known to us only from the few feeble rays of light which reach us out of the vast depths of space. We seem destined to remain forever cut off and imprisoned on our little planet or at least in our solar system. It is a fate which the human mind, with its urge to know and to explore, finds disagreeable and frustrating.

But although science has done much to bring living things and human beings within the realm of natural law, it leaves the wider questions of whence, where, and wherefore unanswered. It has made great progress with the mechanical and chemical aspects of life—though much remains to be learnt—but a profound and still unbridged gulf remains between the outer world as it is interpreted by science, and the inner world of sensations, feelings, perceptions, and thoughts.

It is because of this inner world and the transformations of experience which occur in it that the life of man differs from all other kinds of living, and especially from the automatic and mechanical. It is precisely because in this inner world the outer world is reduced to some sort of order and meaning, and thereby becomes understandable, that human life is dynamic and creative, and is able to transform the world in which it lives. It has given rise to all the strange modes of living found in human societies and the many fantastic adventures of human history. It has also given rise to man's supreme effort to understand himself and his universe and to all his creations.

The triumphs of science have given human beings a feeling of pride in this ability and power, which in recent times and in some exponents can only be described as an intellectual arrogance which is not justified by the facts. What has been found out, impressive as it is, is perhaps not extensive compared with the scale and complexity of the phenomena with which man is confronted. Individual life is still essentially frail and unprotected, and also temporary. Human beings still need to seek for meaning and inspiration to guide their individual lives. Human societies still painfully attempt to achieve ways of harmonizing the often contradictory objectives of individuals and nations.

The unstable nature of human societies shows that an enduring solution has rarely been found. In limited places and times, it may be, a solution has been achieved, but even then there is no guarantee that it will last, because the individuals of a community are always changing and every new generation, like every individual, has to make its own adjustment between the desires of the individual and the demands of society. Social life is always therefore a state of unstable equilibrium, which is easily destroyed by destructive forces inside and from without. Enduring societies are those with a symbolic framework strong enough to mould the new generation into the continuing pattern while leaving enough individual freedom to provide for initiative and development and happiness.

Science cannot provide the integrations required for these purposes, but it can help by providing clarity and knowledge, by tracing the causes and effects of social phenomena, by bringing hidden relationships into the open, by providing at least some sort of objective criteria by which proposals can be judged. The clarification of relationships by science is itself a force in human affairs, because causes can only be supported and can only win approval by being made understandable, and in the long run in the modern world it is probably true to say that no institutions will last which cannot withstand the kind of objective examination which science provides. One great need at the present time is a greater understanding of human beings physically, mentally, and as members of society. This knowledge will not in itself give rise to satisfying lives, nor will it by itself solve the great difficulties of human life, but it could provide the necessary raw material and background for new adjustments and new relationships, and possibly in the end a new synthesis.

A SHORT LIST OF BOOKS

So MANY excellent books, which undoubtedly contribute something to the appreciation of what is going on in science and thought, are being published on every subject at the present time, that no one can read more than a tiny fraction of them: and many valuable ideas are produced which make no lasting impression. It is true that newspapers and weekly journals give some idea of the contents of newly published books in their reviews, and that this means of conveying information is taking the place of reading the books themselves and is also for many people the main source of their general information: but the information obtained in this way is necessarily disjointed and fragmentary. The object of this book has been to put together many subjects in a connected way, but it has of necessity dealt with many topics only very sketchily, and readers may like to know where to look to get further information and to find more thorough discussions (not necessarily agreeing with the author) of the subjects which have been discussed.

The following list of books, mostly of a nontechnical character, is not meant to be comprehensive. It consists mainly of works which I have found interesting and stimulating.

CHAPTERS I, II

H. BUTTERFIELD: *The Origins of Modern Science* (Bell)
P. G. FRANK: *Modern Science and its Philosophy* (Oxford)
J. JEANS: *Physics and Philosophy* (Cambridge University Press)
A. N. WHITEHEAD: *Science and the Modern World* (Bell)
A. N. WHITEHEAD: *Adventures of Ideas* (Cambridge University Press)
E. WHITTAKER: *Space and Spirit* (Nelson)

CHAPTERS III, IV, V

J. A. V. BUTLER: *Man is a Microcosm* (Macmillan)
J. HUXLEY: *Evolution: The Modern Synthesis* (Allen & Unwin)

W. O. KERMACK AND P. EGGLETON: *The Stuff We're Made of* (Arnold)
C. S. SHERRINGTON: *Man on his Nature* (Cambridge University Press)
M. V. TRACEY: *Proteins and Life* (Pilot Press)

CHAPTER VI

W. R. ASHLEY: *Design for a Brain* (Chapman & Hall)
J. A. BIERENS DE HAAN: *Animal Psychology* (Hutchinson's University Library)
G. RYLE: *The Concept of Mind* (Hutchinson)
W. SLUCKIN: *Minds and Machines* (Pelican)
N. TINBERGEN: *The Study of Instinct* (Oxford University Press)
W. GREY WALTER: *The Living Brain* (Duckworth)
N. WIENER: *Cybernetics* (Wiley)
N. WIENER: *The Human Use of Human Beings* (Wiley)
J. Z. YOUNG: *Doubt and Certainty in Science* (Blackwell)

CHAPTER VII

K. J. W. CRAIK: *The Nature of Explanation* (Cambridge University Press)
K. KAFFKA: *Principles of Gestalt Psychology* (Routledge)
M. H. PIRENNE: *Vision and the Eye* (Pilot Press)

CHAPTER VIII

A. D. ADRIAN (Lord Adrian of Cambridge): *Physical Background of Perception* (Oxford University Press)
W. R. BRAIN: *Mind, Perception and Science* (Blackwell)
P. LASLETT: *The Physical Basis of Mind* (Blackwell)
W. P. D. WIGHTMAN: *Science and Monism* (Allen & Unwin)

CHAPTERS IX, X

G. CHILDE: *Man Makes Himself* (Watts)
O. JESPERSON: *Language: its Nature, Development and Origin* (Allen & Unwin)
J. HOLLOWAY: *Language and Intelligence* (Macmillan)
HELEN KELLER: *The Story of My Life* (Doubleday)
R. A. WILSON: *The Miraculous Birth of Language* (Guild Books)

CHAPTER XI

R. BENEDICT: *Patterns of Culture* (Penguin)
F. S. A. DORAN: *Mind: A Social Phenomenon* (Watts)

E. E. Evans-Richard and others: *The Institutions of Primitive Society* (Blackwell)

J. G. Frazer: *The Golden Bough* (Abridged ed. Macmillan)

J. G. Frazer: *Adonis: A Study of the History of Oriental Religion* (Thinker's Library)

W. Howells: *Primitive Man and his Religions* (Gollancz)

E. O. James: *The Beginnings of Religion* (Hutchinson)

R. Karsten: *The Origins of Religion* (Kegan Paul)

B. Malinowski: *Magic, Science and Religion* (Beacon Press and Doubleday)

B. Malinowski: *The Myth in Primitive Psychology* (Kegan Paul)

M. Mead and N. Cullas: *Primitive Heritage* (Gollancz)

H. J. Rose: *Ancient Greek Religion* (Hutchinson)

J. Rumney and J. Maier: *The Science of Society* (Duckworth)

B. Spencer and F. T. Gillen: *The Arunta; A Study of a Stone-Age People* (Macmillan)

B. Spencer and F. T. Gillen: *Native Tribes of Central Australia*

G. C. Valliant: *The Aztecs of Mexico* (Penguin)

Chapter XII

Will Durant: *The Story of Civilization*, Vols I and II (Simon & Schuster)

E. S. Edwards: *The Pyramids of Egypt* (Penguin)

Guthrie: *The Greeks and their Gods* (Methuen)

H. D. F. Kitto: *The Greeks* (Penguin)

Bertrand Russell: *History of Western Philosophy* (Allen & Unwin)

Chapters XIII, XIV

C. A. Coulson: *Science and Christian Belief* (Oxford)

A. MacBeath: *Experiments in Living* (Macmillan)

F. S. C. Northrop: *The Logic of the Sciences and the Humanities* (Macmillan)

M. Polanyi: *The Logic of Liberty* (Routledge and Kegan Paul)

Bertrand Russell: *Impact of Science on Society* (Allen & Unwin)

G. Bernard Shaw: *Everybody's Political What's What?* (Constable)

C. H. Waddington: *The Scientific Attitude* (Penguin)

C. H. Waddington and others: *Science and Ethics* (Allen and Unwin)

A. N. Whitehead: *Religion in the Making* (Cambridge University Press)

Chapter XV

J. C. Flugel: *Man, Morals and Society* (Duckworth)
S. Freud: *Totem and Taboo* (Kegan Paul)
S. Freud: *Beyond the Pleasure Principle* (Hogarth)
S. Freud: *Outline of Psychoanalysis* (Hogarth)
S. Freud: *Civilisation and its Discontents* (Hogarth)
S. Freud: *Psychopathology of Everyday Life* (The Macmillan Co. and Penguin)
E. Jones: *Sigmund Freud: Life and Works* (Hogarth)
J. Parsons: *The Springs of Conduct* (Churchill)
H. Puner: *Freud* (Grey Walls Press)

Chapter XVI

E. Casirer: *An Essay on Man* (Yale University Press)
R. G. Collingwood: *Speculum Mentis* (Oxford University Press)
R. E. M. Harding: *An Anatomy of Inspiration* (Heffer)
F. Howes: *Man, Mind and Music* (Secker and Warburg)
H. Read: *The Meaning of Art* (Penguin)
H. Read: *Philosophy of Art* (Faber)
D. F. Tovey: *The Integrity of Music* (Oxford University Press)
L. L. Whyte: *Aspects of Form: A Symposium of Form in Nature and Art* (Lord Humphries)

ACKNOWLEDGEMENTS

I have to acknowledge permission to quote from the following works, which has been granted by the respective authors or publishers:

ERNST CASSIRER: *An Essay on Man* (Yale University Press)

E. V. RIEU (translation): *The Iliad* (Penguin Books Ltd.)

P. VALÉRY: *Reflections on the World Today* (Thame and Hudson Ltd.)

MARGARET MEAD: *Coming of Age in Samoa* (W. Morrow & Co., New York, and Curtis Brown Ltd.

HELEN KELLER: *The Story of My Life* (Doubleday & Co., New York)

FRANK HOWES: *Man, Mind and Music* (Martin Secker & Warburg)

SIR JAMES FRAZER: *The Golden Bough* (Macmillan & Co.)

B. MALINOWSKI: *Magic Science and Religion* (Beacon Press, Boston)

S. FREUD: *Collected Papers* and *Beyond the Pleasure Principle* (Hogarth Press)

A. N. WHITEHEAD: *Religion in the Making* (Cambridge University Press)

BERNARD SHAW: *Everybody's political what's what?* (The Society of Authors and the Public Trustee)

GERALD HEARD: *The Riddle of the Flying Saucers* (Carroll & Nicholson & Harpers)

D. H. LAWRENCE: *Fantasia of the Unconscious* (W. Heinemann Ltd. and the executors of Mrs Frieda Lawrence's Estate)

R. A. WILSON: *The Miraculous Birth of Language* (J. M. Dent and Sons)

Earlier versions of Chapters 7 and 8 appeared first in *Science News*, 22 and 34 (Penguin Books)